YANGTSE INCIDENT

"Have rejoined the Fleet . . . God save the King"

YANGTSE INCIDENT

THE STORY OF H.M.S. Amethyst
April 20, 1949, to July 31, 1949

By
LAWRENCE EARL

With a Foreword by
Commander J. S. KERANS R.N. D.S.O.

GEORGE G. HARRAP & COMPANY LTD
LONDON   SYDNEY   TORONTO   BOMBAY

To
H. F. W.

First published 1950
by GEORGE G. HARRAP & CO. LTD
182 High Holborn, London, W.C.1

Dewy Decimal classification: 951.042

*Composed in Fournier type and printed by Western Printing Services, Ltd,
Bristol. Made in Great Britain*

FOREWORD

In April 1949 the Chinese People's Liberation Army swept south across the great natural barrier of the Yangtse river in their drive against the Kuomintang armies of Generalissimo Chiang Kai-shek. The peaceful world of this country was broken when it was announced that one of H.M. ships, when on a routine mission to Nanking, had been driven ashore by heavy gunfire, with considerable loss of life.

This ship was H.M.S. *Amethyst*; further concern was evident when casualties and damage were sustained by H.M. ships *London*, *Black Swan*, and *Consort*, who gallantly attempted to come to the succour of the stricken frigate.

This story deals only with H.M.S. *Amethyst*, but tribute must be paid to the many officers and men on the Far East Station ashore and afloat who spared nothing in their endeavours to assist us in the Yangtse river. *Amethyst* owes much to the constant advice and wise counsel of the Commander-in-Chief, Far East Station, Admiral Sir E. J. Patrick Brind, K.C.B., C.B.E.; the Flag Officer Second-in-Command Vice-Admiral A. C. G. Madden, C.B., C.B.E.; H.B.M. Ambassador Sir Ralph Stevenson, G.C.M.G.; and the personnel of H.M. Embassy at Nanking and the Consulate-General at Shanghai.

Incidents such as the one described in this book are, in times of peace, extremely rare, and, in fact, *Amethyst's* stay in the Yangtse-kiang has no parallel in history. The fact that every one on board the frigate, from the oldest to the youngest, faced the situation with poise and equanimity was indeed salutary and our greatest asset.

The spirit of leadership and devotion to duty was fully exemplified by officers and senior ratings; and this, after all, is the fundamental basis of naval training and the essence of everything that the Royal Navy has stood for in the past, stands for at the present time, and will stand for in the future.

One and all, *Amethyst's* ship's company has shown that courage and fearlessness in adversity are still the finest attributes of the British peoples. Teamwork and co-operation were predominant from the start to the finish. Without this bond of fellowship all might well have been lost. That no link in the chain was broken made the sum-total of conduct on the ship during a trying time a first-class effort.

Most of us who took part in the action which has become known as the Yangtse Incident of 1949 are now separated and will go our devious ways, whether in civilian life or in the Service. I wish all my comrades the best of luck in the future. It was both an honour and a pleasure to serve with them all.

Commander, R.N.

PREFACE

SINCE I was not in *Amethyst* when she sailed up the Yangtse that April day in 1949 this book is primarily the result of interviewing many members of the ship's company after the action was over. It is, I think, none the less factual because of that. In all, I spoke to no fewer than thirty-six officers and men whose duties had scattered them through all parts of the ship. I checked and cross-checked their stories, not because I doubted any of them, but because, in the heat of action, with shells bursting inward, with disaster close at hand, with excitement at boiling-point and fear never far away, details are apt to go unnoticed by some and scraps of conversation to be forgotten for ever. I talked to these men who were there, to many of them for several hours each, and to some for periods of up to four days; and they dug deep into their memories and made the telling of this story possible.

To Commander Kerans and to Lieutenant Weston I owe special thanks, since it was they who helped me tie together all the loose ends; but to each of the others, too numerous to list, I am deeply grateful. The Department of Naval Information of the Admiralty was most helpful and co-operative in getting the necessary permissions and in lighting my way.

Finally, I want to express thanks to my wife Jane for her keen yet kindly criticism of my writing of the story.

L. E.

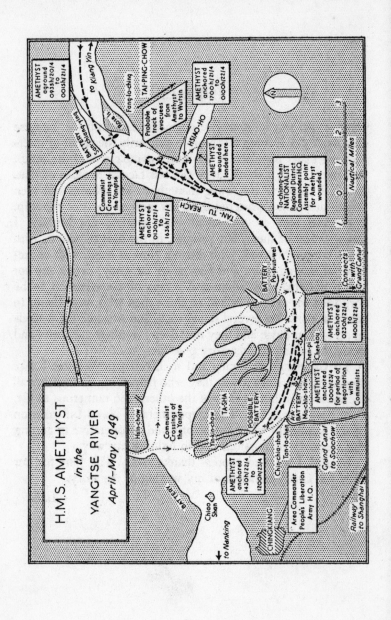

H.M.S. AMETHYST
in the
YANGTSE RIVER
April–May 1949

Nautical Miles
3 2 1 0 1

AMETHYST aground 0935h/20/4 to 005lh/21/4

to Kiang Yin

TAI-PING-CHOW

Fang-lo-ching

BATTERY Su-chiang-yin

Probable track of evacuees from Amethyst to Wutsin

AMETHYST anchored 1700h/21/4 to 0100h/22/4

Amethyst to Wutsin

HSIAO-HO

Communist Crossings of the Yangtse

AMETHYST wounded landed here

AMETHYST anchored 0130h/21/4 to 1636h/21/4

TAN-TU REACH

Ta-chiao-chen NATIONALIST Regional District Commander H.Q. Assembly point for Amethyst wounded.

BATTERY Fu-shun-wei

Connects with Grand Canal

AMETHYST anchored 0230h/22/4 to 1400h/22/4

Chen-Piao Chen-Kiau

AMETHYST anchored 1200h/23/4 for period of negotiation with Communists

Ma-chia-chow

A.A. BATTERY

POSSIBLE BATTERY

TA-SHA

Communist Crossings of the Yangtse

Tin-in-chow

Hsin-chow

Chin-chia-shan Tan-tachen

AMETHYST anchored 1430h/22/4 to 1200h/23/4

BATTERY

Chiao Shan

to Nanking

CHINKIANG

Area Commander Peoples Liberation Army H.Q.

Grand Canal to Soochow

Railway to Shanghai

CONTENTS

9

ILLUSTRATIONS

MAPS

British ships of war coming for no hostile purpose, or being engaged in the pursuit of pirates, shall be at liberty to visit all ports within the dominions of the Emperor of China, and shall receive every facility for the purchase of provisions, procuring water, and, if occasion require, for the making of repairs. The Commanders of such ships shall hold intercourse with the Chinese authorities on terms of equality and courtesy.

Article 52, Treaty of Peace, Friendship, and Commerce between Great Britain and China, signed at Tientsin, June 26, 1858

Chapter One

WHY?

Shortly after nine o'clock on the morning of the 20th of April, 1949, H.M.S. *Amethyst*, a neat, grey frigate of the Royal Navy, ploughed through the murky waters of the Yangtse river. Behind her she left a swirling wake of mist.

To *Amethyst's* port, along the rolling south bank of China's great waterway, Nationalist troops watched for the coming Communist attack with a fatalistic fear. To her starboard, along the flatter, swampier, mist-shrouded north bank, green-clad men of the Chinese People's Liberation Army massed assault craft and manned sullen guns.

Suddenly these guns spat forth flame and high explosives. It was twenty minutes past nine. *Amethyst* was hit again and again. Before the shooting stopped, later that day, twenty-three of the one hundred and eighty-three aboard were dead or dying, and thirty-one were wounded. The little ship was hit fifty-three times.

The grim and unexpected news was flashed by wireless to Britain. That was not all. Under the muzzles of Communist batteries *Amethyst* could not, it seemed, avoid destruction. At best, she faced capture by troops with whom Britain was not at war.

Why, they wondered at home, had it happened? Who was to blame?

Some days previously the Communists of the north had issued an ultimatum to the Nationalists of the south. "Agree to an unopposed crossing of the Yangtse by April the 20th," the demand went. "If not, on the 21st we will launch a full-scale offensive against you." Even so, it appeared that *Amethyst*, with full clearance from the then Government of China, had more than fourteen hours of grace in which to reach Nanking with supplies for the British Embassy and for a routine change-over with *Consort*, a 1710-ton British destroyer.

Even to-day it is not clear why *Amethyst* was fired upon. Was the first salvo a deliberate, sneering affront to Britain and the Royal Navy?

Or, as *Amethyst's* First Lieutenant, Geoffrey Lee Weston, believes, did the Communist gunners mistake the frigate's up-river movement for the double betrayal and attempted escape of a Chinese Nationalist warship which had previously agreed, for a price, to remain at the near-by river-port of Kiang Yin and fight on the Communist side?

Were the Communists, trigger-happy and jumpily awaiting the order to lay down a barrage for their scheduled crossing of the river at this point in great strength, too ready to fire at anything that moved which they could not immediately identify as their own?

Yet, if either excuse is valid—and in the tense, explosive region of a battlefront the tendency is to shoot first and question later—why, after the *Amethyst* was identified, did the Chinese Communists keep her cooped up, under threat of destruction, during the endless, simmering months of May, June, and July?

These questions may never satisfactorily be answered. But when the story of *Amethyst's* Yangtse adventure is condensed into the distant and impersonal print of history her reckless,

*Reducing Top-weight
early in July* 1949

*"Operation Oil"—
Hot, Sweaty Work*

Junk Traffic sailing past

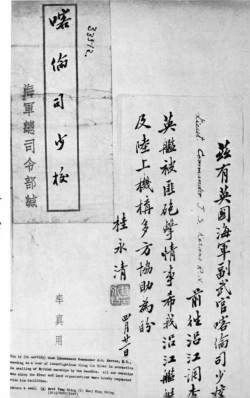

*Kerans' Letter of
Authority from the
Chinese Admiral*

breathless, night-long dash to safety under virtually impossible conditions may be judged the most gallant mass escape ever made.

This is simply a factual account of the little ship's fateful hundred and one days, and of the adventures which befell her company. By inference it is also an appreciation of Royal Navy training, which prepares officers and ratings to suffer disaster and conquer in the end.

Chapter Two

THE BEGINNING

The Yangtse is a river which suffers from seasonal floods. Loosed by the melting snows in high and distant Tibet, by the summer monsoon, and now and then by the sudden turbulence of a typhoon, the floods stir up the sand and mud along the river-bottom.

The quickened current pushes the whirling particles downstream. The soft floor of the river heaves and changes. Channels shift. A course safe for shipping in one season becomes perilous or impassable for anything but flat, shallow-draught native sampans in another. Navigation is often treacherous under all conditions but the best, and ships do not normally try to travel the Yangtse by night. In addition, at this time the Nationalists had forbidden ships to move after dark.

That is why *Amethyst*, a three-hundred-foot frigate, with two Chinese river pilots aboard, dropped anchor at Kiang Yin, one hundred miles up from the river's yawning, island-divided mouth late in the afternoon of April the 19th.

She had left Shanghai that morning, carrying a youngish crew, including sixteen boy-seamen fresh both to the ship and to the Far East Station. The sixteen had started up-river anticipating strange and exotic sights—queer-shaped temples with their pagodas reaching up against the deep orange of a setting sun; bamboo houses standing ridiculously on stilts in the shallow water; laughing, almond-eyed girls at the river's shores. Instead they had seen flat and empty paddy-fields, a few stunted trees, and, in the blue distance, a low, uninteresting line of hills. Tugs hauling rafts of logs down-river had passed them. Now and then they came to poor, mud-coloured villages. That was all.

Anchored at Kiang Yin, Lieutenant-Commander Bernard Morland Skinner, *Amethyst's* captain, spoke to his men over the ship's intercom. "The Chinese Communists are dug in along the north bank," he said. The intercom. gave a peculiarly tinny quality to his voice. "They have already shelled the Nationalists on this side of the river. We are in the fighting zone."

A mild buzz of excitement ran through the ship's company. There was a strange feeling among the men, a feeling of danger by proxy. The danger was real enough, of course, to the Chinese Nationalists and to their several warships anchored near by; but how could it seriously threaten any of them?

Still, even proxy danger brought with it a minor thrill. It would be worth writing home about.

Petty Officer David Heath looked towards the far north shore. Heath's broad shoulders made him appear less than his five feet eight inches. His chest left little room to spare in his tropical shirt. His nose, which looked as if it had once been broken, gave his face a pleasantly rough-hewn appearance. He spoke aloud what the men were thinking.

"They're pretty close," he murmured, shaking his head. "Pretty close."

As dusk rolled in one of the Nationalist gunboats signalled *Amethyst* to darken ship. She did so. That night some of the new boys slept fitfully.

With the dawn *Amethyst's* bow sliced through the current up the river. By the time Kiang Yin was an hour behind her fog had settled silently round the frigate, obscuring both banks of the Yangtse.

"We anchor now," one of the Chinese pilots said nervously. He did not trust the river, and he trusted it even less in the fog. *Amethyst* dropped her hook.

By half-past seven the sun had begun to burn its way through the mist, and the frigate pushed on. Even to the boy-seamen the imminent, pleasurable feeling of mild danger seemed to evaporate with the fog. The day was becoming warm.

Until half-past eight activity on board the ship went along

B

the well-worn channels of routine. Lieutenant-Commander Skinner had been supplied at Hong Kong with intelligence which enabled him to calculate that *Amethyst* was now approaching a sector of the river heavily gunned on the Communist-held north bank.

Engineroom Artificer Leonard Williams, a thirty-year-old Felixstowe man, went on watch in the engineroom at eight o'clock, taking over from Engineroom Artificer Gerald Graham.

"The order has come down to increase from a hundred and eighty to two hundred and sixty revolutions at half-past eight," Graham said.

This meant *Amethyst's* eleven-knot economical cruising-speed would be raised to a more urgent sixteen knots. At eight-thirty the ship would be passing a Communist battery, and the increase in speed was merely a precautionary measure. Williams hummed at his work.

Stoker Mechanic Samuel ("Paddy") Bannister, a pink-faced Belfast boy of twenty-one, was eating breakfast of beans on toast and tea with Owen Aubrey, Kenneth Winfield, and some other shipmates. They were idly discussing their scheduled arrival at Nanking later that day.

Leading Seaman Leslie Frank, a veteran who had seen twenty-four years of service in the Navy, was in the wheel-house with Chief Petty Officer Rosslyn Nicholls and Ordinary Seaman Reginald Wright. Nicholls, as coxswain, was at the wheel. Wright was stationed at the port telegraph, and Frank at the starboard telegraph. It was quiet in the wheelhouse, and even the steady pulsing of the engines seemed far away. Frank was thinking that in another year he would be out of the Navy. He would be with his Dublin-born wife, Kathleen, and he would be discovering what it was to make a living in Civvy Street. Perhaps he was a little apprehensive. What else did he know but the Navy?

Petty Officer Heath, closed up in the transmitting station, the brain-centre of the ship's six four-inch guns, could see nothing beyond the four walls of that room.

Leading Seaman Thomas Mullins and the other gunners were at their stations, relaxing around their twin-mounted weapons in the brightening sunshine. Petty Officer George Griffiths was busily cooking a joint of beef in the galley for the midday meal.

All was well.

At half-past eight, still at breakfast, Bannister happened to glance out of a starboard port. He was just in time to see a giant mushrooming of water not more than twenty yards from the ship.

"What the——" he said, and excitedly ran over to the port for a closer look.

At that moment Winfield yelled from the other side of the ship, "Hey! Somebody's shooting at us!" His deep voice carried a note of surprise.

Aubrey spoke quietly, as if it were of no great importance. "If they come any closer," he said, "we'll have one inboard in a minute."

Breakfast was quite forgotten.

In the wheelhouse Frank, a solidly built man of forty-two, heard the whistling of the shells as they passed overhead. The crow's-feet at the corners of his pale-blue eyes seemed to deepen as he frowned. The ports of the wheelhouse were covered with iron deadlights, and it was impossible to see out. The shells sounded very close.

Frank shifted from one foot to the other. He wished he could see what was going on outside. "What the hell is happening?" he demanded irritably.

Nicholls, tense at the wheel, trying to catch orders as they came down the voice-pipe from the bridge, did not reply. He was quite tall and slender, with a long, serious face which made him, at times, look almost middle-aged. He was in his late twenties.

Frank thought: "What the hell! It's probably just some Communist shells passing over our heads to the Nationalist bank of the river. It isn't our war."

"Full ahead, both!"

The brisk order came down the voice-pipe from Lieutenant-Commander Skinner. Frank translated it to the starboard telegraph. Wright sent the message down to the port engine. The ship leaped ahead.

Below, in the engineroom, the whining of the turbines tended to drown all outside sounds. Williams did not hear the shells falling round the ship.

Meanwhile Telegraphist Jack French, a tall, dark young man with rather soft eyes, had just come off the morning watch. He was feeling ravenously hungry, and lost no time in getting down to the mess-deck. There he made himself a "herringsin" sandwich, the principal ingredient of which was a tinned herring in tomato sauce.

"I didn't hear any shellfire," he said later, when he was told what had happened.

With the first shots Heath, through his earphones, had heard Lieutenant-Commander Skinner hastily ordering Union Jacks to be unfurled down the sides of the ship, where they could hardly escape being seen. Then he heard Skinner say, "Director, get on to target!"

Because it is difficult, if not impossible, to engage a target which has not yet been located this order was not carried out. The Communist batteries here were completely hidden in low scrub. In this preliminary bombardment (of which no account appeared in the Press at the time) no one was hurt; no damage was done. The Communist guns stopped firing after about twelve rounds. Perhaps by then the gunners had recognized the unfurled Union Jacks.

Amethyst's guns were unloaded. They had not been fired. Later Lieutenant Weston said, "No one was worried. You don't worry until you're hit." He added, ruefully, "I remember hoping vaguely during the firing that one of the shots would just scrape the ship's side. We had exceeded our paint allowance, and I knew if this happened we would get more."

Chapter Three

STUCK

By a quarter to nine the danger seemed well over. Winfield, who had rushed to the upper deck to see what was going on, felt sufficiently reassured to return to the mess-deck to take a shower-bath.

As soon as the firing stopped Lieutenant-Commander Skinner wrote out a signal to be sent to Hong Kong, in which he described what had happened. He sent it down to the wireless office to be coded before transmission. This would take some time. French was called back on duty, before he had the time to make another sandwich, to help Petty Officer Telegraphist Mewse and Leading Telegraphist Crocker in coding the message. Because of what followed this message was never delivered.

At twenty minutes past nine Lieutenant Weston, a rather thick-set officer with a cheerfully pink, full face, stood on B-gun deck, just above the captain's cabin. Beside him Mr Monaghan, the commissioned gunner, was breaking out more ammunition.

A shell whined overhead.

"They've started firing again!" Petty Officer Alfred White announced in a surprised voice.

Amethyst was passing another battery of the Chinese People's Liberation Army. The battery was on a point of land near a village called San-chiang-ying. To port was Rose Island, small, flat, and triangular. Ahead the channel twisted and turned.

"Full ahead, both!" Skinner ordered.

A second later Frank, in the wheelhouse, heard a shattering explosion right upon him. Some one screamed. As Frank felt a swift blow on his back and fell to the floor he saw Nicholls fall to one side, dragging the wheel to port with him. This first hit, as it happened, sealed *Amethyst's* fate.

Frank was dazed. He scrambled to his feet a moment later, wondering what had hit the ship. Nicholls was groaning. He had been seriously hit through his right thigh, and he had a bad gash on his forehead. Frank pulled Nicholls' hand from the wheel and turned the wheel back amidships, hoping to get *Amethyst* back on to the course Nicholls had been steering.

"Wheelhouse to bridge!" he shouted up the voice-pipe. "Wheelhouse to bridge!" But there was no reply.

As soon as the shell had hit the wheelhouse Weston hurried to the bridge. He passed through the wheelhouse on his way.

"I saw various bodies lying about," he reported later. "There were gasps and groans. I was in a hurry."

Weston was gunnery officer as well as First Lieutenant. When he reached the bridge he asked Skinner, who had increased speed, if he could return the fire.

"Yes," Skinner said.

Weston took the 'phone from Ordinary Seaman Albert Driscoll, his communications number. The 'phone connected with the Oerlikons and the larger guns. Driscoll was fair, and his complexion was fresh.

"Open fire!" Weston ordered.

As he handed the 'phone back to Driscoll he heard the ear-shattering crash of an explosion very near at hand. He felt a hot piece of steel biting in through his ribs, and, at the same time, it was as though he had been hit by a heavyweight boxer. He doubled up, and for some time he did not seem able to breathe.

Two more direct hits, one after the other, caught the bridge. The marksmanship of the Communist gunners was all too excellent. Though Weston was dazed, he was dimly aware that the others were falling around him like skittles: Skinner, Lieutenant Mirehouse, the ship's navigator, Lieutenant Berger, Able Seaman Donald Redman, Driscoll, Signalman Dennis

Roberts, and one of the Chinese pilots. They were all hit and on the deck.

"Would you like me to take over, sir?" Weston asked after a while. He found, with a kind of distant, impersonal surprise, that it was hard to speak. Skinner nodded feebly.

There is a small, red indication light in the wheelhouse of *Amethyst* which burns as a warning only when the gyro compass is not functioning. Frank saw that it was burning now.

"Wheelhouse to bridge!" he yelled once more. He was frantic. With the iron deadlights covering the ports and the steel doors shut, he was blind to what was happening outside. He was unable to see where *Amethyst* was headed. Even worse, to make his helplessness complete, it now seemed that he had no voice communication outside the wheelhouse.

Frank took a course on the magnetic compass and put the ship steady on it. Then he clattered up the ladder to the bridge. He saw Skinner, Weston, Berger, Mirehouse, Driscoll, Redman, and Roberts all unconscious or wounded and on the deck. Berger's clothes, except for his trousers and a collar still incongruously around his neck, had been blown clean off him. Frank was struck with the sudden, awful realization that, for the moment at least, the fate of the ship rested squarely in his hands.

From the bridge he saw, with a feeling of shocked horror, that *Amethyst* was heading straight for the bank, which now loomed very close. He slid, almost convulsively, down the ladder into the wheelhouse and pushed the wheel hard over to starboard. He was breathing hard.

Meanwhile, in the transmitting station, Heath's only knowledge of what was going on came through his earphones. He was connected by them to the control office and to the gundirector. Suddenly he heard Weston, who had regained consciousness, speaking to Lieutenant Keir Hett, the young and boyish-looking director-control officer.

"Alarm starboard!" Weston said. After a moment his voice came over the earphones again. Weston was panting heavily, wheezily, like a hurt animal. "Engage target," he said, and gave the bearing. His words were broken by his gusty, uncontrolled breathing, and they were difficult to understand.

"What the devil's the matter with him?" Heath thought. "Is he hit?"

Heath pressed the 'fire' buzzer on Weston's order to do so. He should have heard *Amethyst's* guns roar immediately after. Nothing happened. *Amethyst's* guns were still.

Heath did not know that a shell, bursting into the low power-room, had killed Electrician's Mate Sydney Hicks, and had put the machinery there out of commission. The complicated apparatus for controlling all six guns together, as a single fighting unit, was useless.

Monaghan, standing beside Heath, began to swear quietly but bitterly to himself. "Damn it," he said. "This is the third time I've been out East, and every time I've pulled a packet!" He seemed to take it as a personal affront.

Weston saw that *Amethyst* was heading straight for the shore of Rose Island. He did not know that Frank had momentarily visited the bridge. He began shouting orders down to the wheelhouse to avoid the bank. He felt so certain that *Amethyst* was going aground that he turned to Skinner and asked, "Shall I drop anchor, sir?" He suggested this as an emergency move, thinking that the anchor, hooked to the bottom of the river, might prevent the frigate from running up on the bank, might hold her back like a dog straining against a leash.

Skinner's eyes were shut. Weston then realized that Skinner, a short man who had smiled a lot, was very seriously hurt; there was no use consulting him further about the operation of the ship.

"Full astern, both!" Weston yelled over the voice-pipe.

Frank made a projectile of his stocky figure. He threw it first at the port telegraph and set the pointer at 'full astern.' Then he tried to do the same with the starboard telegraph. He strained at the lever.

It would not budge.

He tried short, violent jerks at it with his whole weight and strength behind each one; but there was no response. The starboard telegraph was jammed.

He was perspiring freely. He tried to get through to the engineroom on the voice-pipe. "Wheelhouse to engineroom!" he called. The sweat ran in rivulets down his dark face. There was a note of frenzy in his voice. "Wheelhouse to engineroom!"

He couldn't get through.

He had a feeling of approaching hysteria, and then, as he felt the ship oozing into the mud, the feeling disappeared. There was no jar, no sudden stop. The frigate was still.

Now that *Amethyst* was stuck in the mud with her stern towards the Communist guns A- and B-guns were no longer able to bear on the target. X-gun, at *Amethyst's* stern, was ordered into local control.

Since the transmitting station was now also of no use, Heath and Monaghan joined the ratings from A- and B-guns on the upper deck. Some of this group backed up X-gun, which was now spitting balefully away, with first aid; others pitched in as ammunition supply-parties. Heath tended to the wounded with Monaghan and seven others. His first patient was Ordinary Seaman Albert Rimmington, from Stoke. The decks were slippery with blood, and the ship smelled of burned powder. Some of the ship's company, blasted out of their normal routine, carried wounded down to the after mess-deck, where there was some measure of protection from the continuing Communist pounding.

It seemed strange to Heath that the sun was still shining brightly.

Weston ordered 'full astern.' This time the engineroom received the order and put it into effect. But it was no good: the ship remained exactly where she was, her bow rammed three feet deep in the soft, sucking river-bottom. *Amethyst*, fast in the mud, was a sitting duck. It seemed surely only a matter of time before she was completely destroyed with all on board. The shells poured in regularly, a maiming hit every minute or less.

There seemed to be no hope at all, or perhaps just one faint ray—that *Consort* would be able to get down-river from Nanking and pull them off the mud. Even then they would have to make a mad dash for the open sea, running a point-blank gauntlet of Communist guns. But first they had to get off the mud.

Would *Consort* come in time?

Chapter Four

OVER THE SIDE

When the 'full-speed' order came down to the engineroom from Lieutenant-Commander Skinner, Williams heard the heavy sound of artillery, over the whine of the turbines, for the first time that morning. Somebody yelled that the shooting was directed straight at *Amethyst*.

At the time of the first hit, on the wheelhouse, the engineer officer, Wilkinson, was in his cabin making out claims for War medals. This was a slow process. He had just completed a claim on behalf of Chief Stoker Aubrey when the first hit shook the ship.

Wilkinson pushed the papers aside and ran towards his action station in the engineroom. He met Engineroom Artificer Stanley Roblin on the way.

Roblin, who was wearing leather tropical sandals, made his way aft to his locker to change into shoes. Just as he bent down to tighten the laces a shell burst through the bulkhead and exploded directly over him, spraying his head and a narrow path down his spine with shell-splinters. He fell unconscious to the deck.

"We were so busy," Williams said afterwards, "that we couldn't get to him just then. When a ship is at full speed the engineroom staff is entirely occupied taking readings of gauges and throttles. We had a full head of steam in the boilers, the throttles were wide open, and we had to keep a close watch to avoid stoppage of machinery."

One young stoker scrambled down the ladder into the engineroom. He had just come down from the upper deck, and was very close to hysteria.

"Blood!" he yelled. "There's blood everywhere!"

"All right." Wilkinson spoke to him quietly, reassuringly. "Keep it under your hat." Wilkinson, at thirty-six, was a veteran. He had a homely face that never seemed to lose its repose. The boy was only nineteen. He seemed to steady down.

"Yes, sir!" he said.

John Joseph McNamara, a medium-sized Londoner with an Irish face and a round, button nose, was the only European civilian on board *Amethyst*. Every British naval vessel from a frigate and larger has a N.A.A.F.I. canteen manager aboard who sells everything to the ship's company from razor-blades to ice-cream. He sells tinned foods for extra messing, fresh vegetables for salads, sweets and tobacco. While it is true that these canteen managers are, technically, civilians, they are subject to the captain's orders while on board ship.

McNamara's action station was in the sick bay. One of the first shells crashed into the sick bay, which was occupied by not only McNamara, but Surgeon Lieutenant John Alderton, Sick-berth Attendant Thomas Baker, and Boy-seaman Maurice Barnbrook as well. The shell killed Barnbrook outright, but by some fluke the doctor, Baker, and McNamara escaped without a scratch.

In the engineroom, shortly after half-past nine, Williams saw the port telegraph move to 'stop.' The starboard telegraph, however, remained at 'full speed.' This was an extraordinary combination in the circumstances. Then Williams saw that some one in the wheelhouse was trying to force the starboard telegraph, without success, to 'stop,' to match the port telegraph.

On his own initiative Williams stopped both engines. It was fortunate that he did so. If he had not *Amethyst* would without doubt have driven even more deeply into the mud.

As soon as Weston saw that *Amethyst* was firmly aground he left the bridge. He went down through the wheelhouse, and saw that Wright, standing now at his port telegraph, was mortally wounded.

"Come on, lad," Weston said gently, "I'll give you a hand."

He tried to carry Wright down the hatch to the next deck for medical aid. He had forgotten his own wound in his eagerness to help. Suddenly Weston felt his shoulder go, completely out of his control and without strength.

Wright slid down the ladder into a rating who had been standing at its foot. The rating took him down the next flat to the sick bay.

An hour later Wright died in the arms of his friend Electrical Artificer Lionel Chare. His last thoughts were of his home and family. "Find my photograph album," he told Chare, "and send it to my mother." Then he was still for ever.

It was thirty-five minutes past nine when *Amethyst* went aground. Afterwards many of her ship's company found it impossible to credit that it had all happened so very soon after the opening of the action. Too much had happened in too short a time.

Stores Petty Officer John Justin McCarthy, a Navy veteran of eleven years' service, saw gun-flashes on the north bank after *Amethyst* ran aground on Rose Island. The flashes were directly astern, and seemed to him to come from behind some mud-coloured huts. The guns themselves were well concealed behind the huts, and only the uncomfortably regular flashes were visible. McCarthy was normally light-hearted, almost happy-go-lucky. He did not feel that way now.

Later he was kept busy helping with the wounded. He had passed a first-aid course. As he walked along the mess-deck and stepped over one of the wounded men lying down on the deck he looked down and saw that it was Leading Seaman Cyril Williams.

"Mind my leg, Jack," Williams said. He did not realize that he had lost both his feet.

"Sure, Bungy," McCarthy said.

All Navy men with the surname of Williams are nicknamed Bungy, just as all stores ratings, like McCarthy, are called Jack

Dusty, or simply Jack. There is an infinite variety of Navy nicknames: Liverpool men are called Scouse, canteen managers are named Damager, signalmen are referred to as Bunting-tosser, and so on.

Then Williams said, "For God's sake, Jack, how about getting up the rum? It's due at eleven, and it must be getting pretty close to that now."

"I'll have it up in a few minutes, Bungy," McCarthy promised.

When the second shelling began Bannister was below-decks with Leading Stoker Mechanic Ormrod.

"Let's go up to see what's happening," Ormrod suggested, unable to contain his excitement.

"Sure," Bannister agreed. He was a little scared, but he didn't want to admit it. This was his first action.

Ormrod went ahead, with Bannister about to follow, when a shell crashed through the low power-room bulkhead. This was on the starboard side of *Amethyst*. Bannister heard an explosion, and seemed to be completely enveloped in a great, blinding flash of light. Suddenly he couldn't breathe.

Blood seemed to be spurting all over him. He thought at first that he had been hit in the face. He hadn't. A shell-splinter had entered his chest, and was lodged tightly against the right branch of his windpipe. He looked up, and saw a rating standing in the doorway of the power-room, his face and one arm covered with blood. He couldn't make out who it was.

Bannister was down on the deck, and he couldn't remember falling. He tried to get to his feet and walk. He couldn't manage it. He crawled painfully round to the protection of the port passage, pushing himself awkwardly along, crablike, with his legs. Then he noticed that others who were not wounded were crawling too. They did not want to be hit by flying splinters.

One of the stokers yelled at him, "You look bad, mate. Go back to the after mess-deck and lie down."

Somehow, gasping and constantly fighting the pain, Bannister managed to crawl to the after mess-deck. Half a dozen other wounded men were already there. They were lying on the floor, as they had been instructed to do, to reduce the chances of being hit again. They could not use the sick bay, which had been left a shambles by the shell which had killed Barnbrook. Stoker Mechanic Arthur Brown, a friend of Bannister's, was helping some of them.

Bannister's face was contorted with pain. "Brownie," Bannister said, "will you put a piece of cloth in my mouth, so I can bite on it, like, and kill the pain?"

"Sure, Paddy. What's wrong?"

"I can't breathe."

Brown rolled up a piece of gauze for Bannister to bite on. He put a lifebelt under his head for a pillow. Alderton was administering morphia to the men by hypodermic to kill the pain.

He gave a shot to Bannister. For a long time it didn't seem to have any effect. Bannister continued to bite hard on the wad of gauze. He made a faint, hissing noise as he breathed, and little beads of perspiration broke out on his forehead, gathered into larger drops, and fell in rivers down his nose and along the sides of his face.

At about twenty minutes to ten on the morning of the 20th of April *Amethyst* sent out this flash signal to all ships in plain, uncoded English:

UNDER HEAVY FIRE. AM AGROUND. LARGE NUMBER OF CASUALTIES.

She also gave her position, but, in the chaos of the moment, gave it incorrectly. The latitude and longitude given in the message would have placed the ship somewhere far from any large body of water, high and dry on the Chinese mainland. After that first message *Amethyst's* power went off. The low power-room had been hit, and, for the time at least, she was without contact with the outside world.

Amethyst's signal was picked up by H.M.S. *Consort*, lying at Nanking, but due to sail later that day after *Amethyst's* expected arrival. The news was relayed to Sir Ralph Stevenson, the British Ambassador, who wasted no time in sending urgent dispatches to the headquarters of Mao Tse-tung, the Communist leader. Stevenson asked for a cease-fire.

One of the several involved in the relaying of that first message from *Amethyst* to the Ambassador was the Embassy's Assistant Naval Attaché, John Simon Kerans. His rank was that of lieutenant-commander. At the time he had no idea how vitally important the *Amethyst* affair would become to him.

For a while after *Amethyst* grounded there was a state of some confusion aboard her. In the wheelhouse Weston spoke urgently to Frank.

"We're aground," he said. "Get a party up on the bridge, and bring the captain and the other wounded to a safer place."

Frank hurried to obey this command. He collected the first six able-bodied men he could find, and with them fetched the wounded from the bridge and the wheelhouse to the after mess-deck. Shells were thudding into the ship all the time. There seemed to be a great deal of disorganized running to and fro on the decks and passageways.

X-gun, firing independently, had got away thirty rounds. Boy Dennis Roberts, a Plymouth lad, had taken cover underneath the Bofors gun on the port side, just behind the funnel. He was looking aft when he saw the bright-yellow flash of a hit on the X-gun flare. Leading Seaman Thomas Mullins was blown clean off the gun platform and on to the deck by the blast. Astonishingly, he was unhurt. He jumped back on to the gun.

Several ratings were handing out ammunition to supply the gun. The automatic hoist wasn't working. Roberts later reported: "I saw the shell burst directly on X-gun then, and splinters flew around like hail."

That second hit on the gun killed Ordinary Seaman Dennis Griffiths and Ordinary Seaman Charles Battams, X-gun's trainer. Splinters wounded Albert Rimmington, Amos Davies, and Gwilyn Stevens. One of the men was killed where he sat, his hands frozen to the training-handle. He appeared to be still on the job.

"Train around!" Mullins yelled at him. "Train around!" Then he saw that the man was dead.

There was a cloud of black smoke shrouding X-gun, and it was out of action for good. None of *Amethyst's* four-inch guns could now be brought to bear on the Communist battery of 75- and 105-mm. guns. If her position had been desperate before it was now surely impossible. She was stuck fast. Neither A- nor B-gun was of any use. And X-gun was wrecked.

The buzz went round the ship. "Our only chance is *Consort*. If she pulls us off the mud we can make a run for it."

Boy Keith Martin went forward after X-gun was hit, and there somebody gave him a rifle. He took cover in the small shipwright's shop, poking his head and shoulders out of the door so that he could fire his rifle. He was shooting at no special target on the north shore: he was just shooting, almost by reflex action.

Somebody yelled, "Repel boarders if they come!" It was Weston, who, with the entire ship's company, expected the Communists to come alongside in boats as a logical follow-up to their attack.

A few feet away from Martin several members of the crew were firing rifles from under the ship's motor-boat. A shell came over and burst. The smoke for a moment obscured the area round the motor-boat. When it cleared Martin saw that the men under the boat were all dead. He rushed to the other side of the ship, retching and feeling ill. Somebody pounced on him there, and told him to help the wounded on the quarterdeck.

Martin was giving one of the wounded a drink of water when another shell hit the quarterdeck, and, suddenly, he couldn't see. He was flat on the deck, with all the wind

C

knocked out of him. "I thought I was dying," he told Bannister later.

He tried, after a time, to open his eyes, and, at first very dimly, then more clearly, he saw men jumping over the side into the swift current of the river. Deciding, correctly, that some one had given an order to evacuate the ship, he slipped over into the water himself, almost without thinking. He did not know then that he was badly wounded in the left thigh.

All this time members of the crew had been issued with Bren guns and other small arms. It was while Wilkinson was helping to distribute these that a shell landed near him. Leslie Crann and Dennis Morgan, both stokers, were killed. Wilkinson heard what he afterwards called "a terrific bang. I felt as if some one had clouted me on the back of the head. My first reaction was to turn round and clout him back. Then I passed out."

Weston, making a round of the ship shortly before ten, found X-gun abandoned. A few bodies were lying round the gun. There was a small fire near by, and the deck was smouldering and one of the bodies was burning. He told Able Seaman Mulley to get a Foamite—a small fire-extinguisher—and, with Mulley's help, Weston put the fire out with it. The ship smelled strongly and acridly of burned powder and burned flesh.

"Start getting some boats lowered," Weston told Berger, who, in spite of serious wounds in the arm, leg, and chest, had been rushing around the ship seeing that Weston's orders were being carried out. "Just in case I decide to evacuate the ship." Weston did not know that all but the small whaler had been splintered by shells. "Besides, it will keep the lads busy. It's no use asking them just to wait around until they're killed." Berger looked a mess, with his clothes blown off and his deep wounds visible.

After the effort of putting out the fire Weston began to feel very faint. He knew that if he didn't sit down he would collapse. Finally he sat down near the funnel on the port side of the upper deck. (For six weeks he had to sleep sitting up. He had shell-splinters through his lung. One piece was buried in his liver.)

Alderton, the doctor, and Baker, the sick-berth attendant, found Weston sitting there.

"Are you coughing blood, Geoff?" Alderton asked.

"A little."

"Well, that's the only thing to worry about—if you're coughing blood." He gave Weston a shot of morphia. He instructed a seaman to bandage Weston's wound.

Berger came along at the run. It was remarkable that he could move about so quickly with his wounds. "Doc," he said, "Mirehouse needs attention on the after flat." Mirehouse was an old Harrovian, and his fellow-officers referred to him good-naturedly as "Sir Richard, the impoverished aristocrat," because he was always borrowing shirts. A shell had hit some storage batteries, and Mirehouse's face had been sprayed with acid. Alderton and Baker finished up with Weston and hurried towards the after flat. They never reached Mirehouse.

A moment later they were both dead. They had walked straight into a bursting shell.

At about half-past ten Weston instructed Petty Officer Henry Freeman and Frank to get a wire ready astern *Amethyst*, so that they would be ready to be towed off by *Consort* when she came.

Frank and Freeman went aft to the starboard side of the quarterdeck and uncovered the hawser wheel. Small-arms fire was whistling around them like jet-propelled wasps, and ricochetting off steel bulkheads with suddenly angrier, higher-pitched whines. The two grabbed the end of the wire and crawled along the quarterdeck, pulling the wire with them. They fastened it in place, but by the time they were finished the small-arms fire was intolerably heavy. They made a quick, scurrying dash for the protected space between the depth-charge racks.

Wiping the sweat from their faces, they grinned sickly at

each other. The racks were covered with canvas, and Frank and Freeman were counting on the depth-charges under the canvas to stop the bullets.

After a moment or two Frank said, "Is there anything in these racks, Harry? I seem to remember we fired some depth-charges not so long ago." He sounded anxious.

Freeman stopped grinning. "Let's have a look."

Frank lifted a canvas cover and dropped it back quickly. There was nothing under the canvas. The pair had been hiding behind the bare canvas, counting on it to stop the Communist bullets.

"Where do we go from here, Les?"

"Make a dash."

Freeman went first. When Frank saw him safely at the far end of the quarterdeck he sprinted the forty or fifty feet of open deck to join him, his short legs flying. Then they stood together, breathing hard.

In a little while Frank reported to Weston that the wire was ready for *Consort* to pull them out of their vice of sucking mud as soon as she arrived. Shortly afterwards he joined Hett in a tour of inspection, to see how much damage had been done below-decks. The wardroom, the first lieutenant's cabin, the doctor's cabin, the navigating officer's cabin, the depth-charge store, were all a shambles.

Weston conferred with Berger.

"Get the ship's company ashore," Weston said; "but leave a steaming party aboard."

Weston now felt sure that the Communists intended to keep on firing until they reduced the ship to wreckage.

He was still sitting on the deck near the funnel. A white sheet of truce was flying overhead. It had been ordered there by Skinner. A little later the Communists started to rake the deck with machine-gun fire. Weston, feeling quite ill, heard somebody near by swearing.

"The bastards!"

Somebody else said, "They'll have something to say about this at home."

Weston crawled into the little radar office for better cover against the small-arms fire, and, after remaining there for a while, moved into the wireless office and sat down with a wheezing, grateful sigh in a canvas-bottomed chair.

It was not much before eleven on that hectic morning when Berger, tall, angular, and crusted with dried blood, moved about the ship, yelling, "Swimmers over the side! Non-swimmers man the whaler!"

This evacuation order meant considerable activity. It also succeeded in fermenting further chaos.

It is laid down in the Royal Navy that in such circumstances —that is, prior to the evacuation of a naval vessel—all code-books and coding-machines must be destroyed. Hett, visiting the wireless office, instructed French, Cook, and Crocker to collect the code-books. Then, while Hett burned the books in the galley stove, the others broke the machines into pieces with mallets and heavy spanners, and threw the pieces into the Yangtse.

Chapter Five

THE ISLAND

Long afterwards it all came back to Bannister like a hazy dream. He remembers, vaguely, being carried to the port side of the quarterdeck by Brown and Patrick Muldoon, and being helped into the whaler. Then Monaghan took charge of the whaler, and four men took the oars. They approached the south bank of the river. The bank loomed high and steep over the small boat.

"I guess it was only four or five feet high," Bannister said afterwards, "but I remember that it looked like a cliff to me. I wondered how we were going to get up it!"

When the whaler was only a few yards from the bank the Communists began to fire on it. The water was pocked with bullets. There was a scramble in the whaler as the men in it reached for the bank, and, suddenly, as a shell landed near by, it capsized. The wounded and unwounded struggled together in the water, splashing and grabbing at the bank. The unhurt helped the others to the bank, and then up it, but Bannister somehow was overlooked. He found himself alone in the water.

A moment later Bannister saw the back of Stoker Mechanic Fred Morrey's head appear over the crown of the bank.

"Morrey!" he croaked. "For God's sake, Morrey!"

Morrey, a small, ginger-haired chap, himself twice wounded in the back, turned his head. With Ordinary Seaman Tom Townsend he crawled back the few feet through the tall grass to the edge of the bank.

"Come on, Paddy," Morrey said. "We'll give you a hand up."

Then Bannister realized that he could move neither his arms

nor his hands. They seemed paralysed. He pushed his way
with his legs until he could lean against the steeply rising bank.

"That's it, Paddy," Morrey said, and reached down with
one hand and cupped it firmly under Bannister's chin.
Townsend reached down and cupped a palm under the other
side of his chin.

They pulled Bannister up the bank that way. The pain in
his chest was excruciating; but he was out of the water and
with the others again.

Bannister, catching what breath he could, heard Monaghan
say, "Keep to the path, men. There are mine-fields around us."
The party of well and wounded began to crawl along the path,
which was trodden, by the passage of countless coolie feet over
the years, into the paddy-field like a long, sinuous trough.
Bannister found that he could now work his arms a little. He
crawled forward on his knees and his elbows.

"You soon crawl," he told Martin a few days later, "when
the bullets are flying around you."

There were six or seven in that first party, crawling in single
file along the sunken path. The high grass gave some cover.
Bannister was breathing on only one lung, and the pain was
getting very much worse. His wounds had started to bleed
again. He slowed down. Morrey crawled back to see what was
keeping him.

"Can I give you a hand, Paddy?"

"No. Go on ahead. I'll follow on behind, like. I can
make it."

Morrey took him at his word, and went on after the others.
Bannister, crawling very slowly, dragging himself along with
more and more difficulty, was aware that the morphia was
wearing off. As it did the pain grew worse and worse. He
made a lot of noise, whistling and wheezing and gasping for
the air which always seemed to elude him. The others drew
farther away.

He put his head on the ground and bit at the roots of the
hip-high grass to try to kill the pain. It seemed to help. After
a while he looked back over his shoulder and saw another,

larger party that must have landed after the first one. Many of this second party were barefoot, and wore only underclothes, which were wringing wet. They had swum ashore, and now they were crawling up behind Bannister. One of the men of this second party heard him gasping, and found him lying, twisted with pain, in the deep grass.

"Can I give you a hand, mate?"

"I'm all right," Bannister insisted. "I'll follow on behind."

One by one they passed him. He felt very weak. He rested there in the high grass, biting at the roots to kill the pain and trying to get some strength back. Then he tried to crawl again, inch by painful inch, on his elbows.

When he looked up young Morrey was crawling back down the path towards him, grinning encouragement. It was good to see him looking so cheerful. Somehow it seemed to help.

"Follow on behind me, Paddy," Morrey said.

Bannister tried; he wanted to follow Morrey very much; but the gap between them widened. Six feet. Nine feet. Twelve feet. After a while he gasped, "Go ahead, mate. I'll rest here a little while." Morrey, who didn't hear him, kept on crawling. Bannister rested.

It was a lovely, sunny morning. After a time his mind must have wandered, for he started to dream. The sky was very blue, and he could see nothing else over the tall, waving grass. Firing had stopped, and from a great distance he could hear a bird singing.

He dreamed that he was somewhere else, somewhere far away in the lovely countryside near his Belfast home, somewhere on holiday and just lying in the sun with nothing to do. Then he heard the shooting break out again, and the beautiful bubble of his dream burst, and he began to crawl again, awkwardly, putting his whole mind to it.

He could not see any of his mates. The song of the bird had disappeared, and he could hear nothing but the firing and his own tortured breathing. After crawling for what seemed to be several hours, but could not actually have been more than ten minutes, he heard voices. The voices seemed to be desperately far ahead.

He could not tell to whom the voices belonged. He could not tell if the words were in English, or where they were coming from. He forced himself up on to his hands, into a kind of upright crouch, and peered over the top of the grass.

Heath was kneeling in the grass only fifteen feet away. He was waving his arms to some one across the quarter-mile-wide arm of the Yangtse that divided Rose Island from the south bank of the river. Moved by some quick and accurate instinct, Heath turned his head.

"Come on, Bannister," he said. He seemed relieved to see the wounded stoker.

With some difficulty Bannister crawled the fifteen feet.

"Have you got any water?" he asked Heath, wheezing it out. His mouth was full of earth and bits of grass and blood, and his face was covered with all three. He wanted to tidy himself up a little, but Heath thought that he wanted the water to drink.

"We'll get you some when we reach the other side," he said. His hair was still wet from his swim.

A sampan, manned by a coolie, was coming towards them across the stretch of water. Some of the others helped Bannister aboard. He dipped his hand into the river, intending to wash the mud and blood from his face.

"Don't drink that, Paddy," Heath said sharply. "You'll get typhoid from that water."

Bannister didn't drink.

The sampan started back across to the south bank. Bannister saw Nationalist soldiers standing there in trenches, holding their rifles at the ready. Up-river two more sampans were crossing at the same speed and in the same direction as his. They were small craft, barely twelve feet long and blunt at both ends, like barges. Each was carrying several *Amethyst* men.

When they landed Stoker "Lofty" Canning, one of Bannister's pals who had crossed in another sampan, came over to shake his hand. Canning had some small splinter-wounds over his left eye. He put one arm around Bannister and helped him to wash, and then helped him to walk the few hundred yards up a path to a collection of wood-and-stone huts which the Nationalists were occupying.

Bannister and the other wounded men were taken into one of the huts. The only light came in through the two open doors, since the windows had been boarded up. The wounded were stretched out on the floor and on the one double bed. Bannister sat on the floor, his knees hunched up in front of him. He felt more comfortable that way.

Morrey, with two gaping holes in his back, was lying on the bed and grinning, as if he had no worries, as if, perhaps, he were at home in Overton, drinking beer in the local with his pals. Two Chinese women, moving silently and solemnly, brought boiled water in pottery bowls for the wounded. The water was still hot and losing little wisps of steam to the cooler, but nevertheless fairly warm, air of the room.

A Nationalist soldier came in and passed out trousers and jackets of padded felt. The clothes of the *Amethyst* men were wet and ripped, and some had practically no clothes on their bodies at all. Bannister was given trousers to replace the blood-soaked pair flapping about his legs. Somebody helped him on with them.

It was in this hut that Bannister first saw Keith Martin. They had both joined the ship at Hong Kong, only a few days before, and had not previously met. Bannister and Martin were the only two in the party seriously enough wounded for stretchers. This gave them a kind of kinship. Martin had a painful splinter-wound on the outer side of his left thigh.

He was about six feet tall and very slender. His body looked as if it could easily be bent into a simple knot without harm. He had a round, shining, button face, a pug nose, and almost Oriental eyes. He was barely seventeen, and looked less, in spite of his height and his eyes. He looked around, full of quiet interest, taking everything in.

Chapter Six

HERE COMES "CONSORT"

Back on the ship, Wilkinson, Aubrey, French, and others of the crew heard Berger yelling, "Swimmers over the side!"

Wilkinson had just regained consciousness, and was still lying on the deck under the starboard Bofors. He pushed himself up, half sitting, half kneeling. Then, from a greater distance than before, he heard Berger again.

"All swimmers over the side!"

Wilkinson got to his feet. He had a feeling of great urgency, and he wasn't quite sure why he had it. He was dazed and weak, and not entirely aware of what he was doing.

He looked for a way to get over the side of the ship, and on the port side, opposite the wireless office, he found a rope dangling down into the hurrying current. He shinned down the rope, sliding down, with not much help from his legs. It was not until some time later that he saw that his hands had been burned quite raw by the rope.

He slipped into the water, and felt the full force of it teasing him downstream. He couldn't use his wounded leg, and the flood current ran at a two-and-a-half-knot speed. He fought against the current, using his strong arms and kicking fast with his good leg. He barely reached the shore, and had to be helped up the bank, panting and weak. Then he rested in the high grass.

French and Crocker had also jumped over the side. French noticed with a feeling of acute helplessness and constricting fear that bullet-splashes churned the water all around him. Because of the stubbornly strong current he swam diagonally up-river, and drifted in with the moving mass of water. Just under the bank he ducked his head behind a rubber dinghy a predecessor had left there. He stayed there long enough to catch his breath; then he scrambled up the steep incline, digging his fingernails into the clay.

He hadn't been on the bank for long when he heard Monaghan shouting desperately for assistance.

"I want volunteers," Monaghan said, "to take the whaler back to the ship for more wounded."

French sat up. He saw two seamen in the whaler and Monaghan at the tiller. He looked around, and saw that he was alone on the bank; the others had crawled along the sunken path or were sheltering in the deep grass. He thought, "I'm the only one around to volunteer. If I don't Monaghan will draw a blank." The current, too, had scattered the swimmers along the shore.

"Hold it!" French shouted, and scrambled down the bank again into the whaler. A quarter of an hour later he was back on the ship. He had been ashore for less than ten minutes, and it would be the last time he would touch dry land for more than a hundred days.

Lieutenant Strain, the flotilla electrical officer, was standing anxiously at the ship's rail as the whaler approached *Amethyst*. He cupped his hands to his mouth. "Is there a telegraphist aboard?" he demanded. All the men from the wireless office, taking Berger at his word, had dropped over the side.

"Yes, sir," French acknowledged. He was pulled up the ship's side by the same rope Wilkinson had slid down, and he and Strain entered the wireless office. There they rigged up emergency batteries and a generator, so that they could make contact with the outside world until the more serious electrical damage could be repaired and the transmission of wireless messages be made, once again, by using the ship's power-plant. They knew now that *Consort* would have to come down the river soon or not at all, and they tried to contact her. They were unable to do so. As French put it when one of the ship's company asked him, "We had no joy."

Aubrey too had jumped over the side at Berger's call. He never reached the shore. No one from *Amethyst* ever saw him again. Whether he drowned in the flood current or was hit by a Communist bullet will probably never be known.

At about noon Griffiths made tea and some sandwiches, but there was no full midday meal. There was still too much confusion aboard to organize it. McNamara filled a bucket, which he used for mixing ice-cream, with chocolate bars, sweets, and cigarettes, and passed the bucket round to the wounded, who helped themselves gratefully. He didn't bother about payment. Later, at Hong Kong, when N.A.A.F.I. checked his books, they found that he was £130 short. In the end the Navy made good the difference for this emergency "free issue."

Wilkinson, resting at full length along the sunken footpath on shore, heard somebody say, "Watch the trip-wires and the mines." He remained where he was. Some time later he saw two Nationalist aircraft firing tracer at the Communist battery from about five hundred feet. Shortly after that a small, grinning bumpkin in the brown uniform of a Nationalist soldier came along and, by a great deal of pointing and gesticulating, showed him where the mines were located. Then the Nationalist dug round a mine with his fingers and cleared the earth away, and picked the mine up and held it out with a kind of childish pride for Wilkinson to examine.

As he held it out he stepped backward perhaps half a pace and balanced precariously on the edge of the river-bank. For a moment it seemed to Wilkinson that the Chinese was certain to fall in, and he wondered wildly whether or not the mine would explode.

"Look out!" Wilkinson yelled.

The little Chinese regained his balance just in time. His grin returned. He placed the mine carefully back into the bed he had dug it from and brushed loose earth over it.

Late that afternoon Wilkinson returned to *Amethyst* by the whaler-ferry Monaghan had organized. The evacuation had been a haphazard one. When he went below he was amazed to find that, although some sixty ratings had left the ship, quite a number of his engineroom staff had remained on board.

Several had been below shutting off steam earlier, and had not heard the evacuation order.

Heath had jumped over the side, and had swum the hundred yards to shore. He had taken off all his clothes, except for an undershirt. In the water he heard the angry whine of bullets over his head.

He scrambled ashore, and waited for other swimmers to join him. Then he led them along the bank, skirting the mine-field. One of *Amethyst's* Chinese cooks had come ashore, fully dressed in his natty blues, including collar and tie. Heath and the other Navy men were crawling along on their stomachs. Not the Chinese cook! A short and roly-poly man, he walked beside them with great dignity and no apparent fear.

"Get down!" Heath yelled. "You want to get hit?"

The Chinese cook shook his head. "No get down," he said stubbornly. "Wearing good suit."

He continued to walk.

All this time the crackle of small arms came from the far bank. When Heath thought he and his party were out of range he stood up in the grass. As soon as he did so two bursts of carbine-fire whistled by. He hit the grass again, hard, knocking the breath out of his body; but otherwise he was unhurt. The bursts had come, totally unexpectedly, from the Nationalist side of the river.

"Maybe they don't realize who we are," somebody said.

It was at this point that Bannister joined Heath's party.

A Chinese mess-boy, also attached to *Amethyst*, said to Heath, "I swim over, yes." It was a statement, not a query. He was a very small youngster, very thin and cheerful. His name was Chan Ping.

"I don't think you ought to try it, Chan. It's a fast current. Damn' fast!"

Chan insisted. "If I get over and wave you come. If they fire at me you stay. Yes." Chan was an employed Chinese mess-boy, and owed the *Amethyst* men no such duty. He has since joined the British Navy as a cook.

He stepped into the water and swam strongly across the

arm of the Yangtse. Soon the Nationalists sent three sampans over for Heath and his men. They were met on the south shore by a Chinese Major who spoke no word of English. He bowed a polite welcome.

Heath explained through the Chinese cook that he wanted medical assistance for the eight wounded men. The Major revealed even white teeth in a broad grin. He led the way along a narrow path for about two hundred yards to a small hut occupied by half a dozen Nationalist soldiers. This was one of their group of outposts. There were, at this time, twenty-four in all in Heath's party; but there were many others from the ship now on shore who would join him later.

When Chan appeared, soaked to the skin, but smiling cheerfully, somebody yelled, "Three cheers for Chan!"

All but the wounded joined in. Chan, his wide face beaming, was obviously as pleased as a small boy who had just been made guest of honour at a surprise party.

A moment later Heath heard renewed artillery-fire. His first horrible thought was that the Communists were finishing off *Amethyst*.

A Nationalist private rushed in, out of breath, and spoke with sing-song excitement to the Major. The Major grinned at Heath. Through the interpreter-cook he said, "British ship coming down-river, shooting at Communists."

Heath could hardly refrain from shouting triumphantly. He knew it must be *Consort*, arriving on the scene at last. "Now for the rescue," he thought. He dashed out of the hut, followed by several of his mates, and ran pell-mell to the river-bank.

It was, indeed, *Consort*. There was a white bone of foam in her teeth, and her guns were blazing away at the Communist battery. She had not yet reached the point in the channel opposite *Amethyst*.

Heath found himself praying, silently, that everything would work out. "Will she get *Amethyst* off?" he wondered hopefully. "Will she escort *Amethyst* safely down to the open sea?"

These questions were soon answered.

Consort, still firing bravely at the Communist battery, sailed past *Amethyst* without reducing speed. Then, while Heath's heart fell and lifted again, she slowed down and, about half a mile below the frigate, came to a stop. She turned and fired her guns at the north bank.

After a while she headed up-river again towards *Amethyst*. Her guns didn't stop shooting for a single moment.

Amethyst meanwhile had raised steam for the getaway. Her ship's company, tensely waiting, buzzed with excitement.

"Do you think she'll have any trouble pulling us off the mud, mate?"

"Get set for some more hits!"

"God, she's taking her own bloody time getting back up!"

Weston had ordered Signalman Dennis Wynn Roberts, who has lost an eye in the shelling, to signal *Consort* by light.

"What's the matter with that eye, Roberts?" Weston asked.

"It's hurt, sir," Roberts said. He didn't know that his eye was gone.

Consort had by then been hit by the Communists on her bridge, wireless office, and wheelhouse. Her captain, Commander I. G. Robertson, had been wounded.

"Is it possible to tow you off?" the light blinked from *Consort*.

Weston thought, "We'll both be blown to bits by the Communist battery." His was a difficult decision to make. He made it; there was no time to think and consider.

"Only if the batteries are silenced first," the *Amethyst* lamp blinked in reply.

The hit in her wheelhouse had crippled *Consort* seriously. It had become obvious that she could not alone silence the shore batteries. She fired a last salvo at the battery and turned back down the river. She steamed away, full ahead, having no other choice. She was travelling at a speed of twenty-seven knots very soon, the highest recorded speed ever made on the Yangtse. She left several fires blazing on the north shore.

After a while the saddened men on *Amethyst* and Heath's party on shore, now swollen by the arrival of other evacuees heard *Consort's* guns again, far down the river. The sound of firing receded gradually. In about half an hour it stopped entirely. There was dead silence now, empty and continuing, for the first time since firing had begun that morning.

It seemed strange, incredibly strange. Now that *Consort* had gone on down no other help could be expected. *Amethyst* and her men were alone and helpless. The ship was still hard aground. The Communist battery had her pinned down by the threat of a point-blank hammering at any time its gunners chose.

"We were sitting there," McNamara said later, "wondering what was going to happen next—and how bad it was going to be."

Chapter Seven

THE PILOT

After *Consort* had passed on down, *Amethyst's* seamen gathered together in little groups, still edgy and excited, to chew over their experiences and their chances of eventual escape.

As was true for many on board, this had been the first time in action for nineteen-year-old Able Seaman John Ray. His boyish face was streaked with dried sweat; his light-brown hair looked as if it had never been combed; there was still a tinge of excitement in his voice. "I didn't feel so good," he told his mates, "but things happened so fast I didn't stop to think of what was going on or what our chances were."

"Me too," Boy Dennis Roberts agreed. He was a fair boy, with blue eyes and an unexpected Roman nose. He was seventeen, and looked younger. "As soon as the shooting stopped, though, I had time to think. I got scared, pretty scared." The deep dimple in his chin had gathered a pocket of burnt powder. "I still am," Ray admitted.

That was the feeling on the ship.

Weston, Berger, Strain, and Hett talked *Amethyst's* position over quietly and seriously. Shells had hit every other office large enough for the purpose, and the wireless-room was now being used as centre of operations.

"Perhaps *Consort* will be back to give us a hand after dark," Hett offered tentatively. His skin was very smooth and pink; his mouth was small and sensitive; and he looked very young and schoolboyish. He was unaware that *Consort*, in her valiant but unsuccessful attempt at knocking out the Communist battery, had suffered serious damage, and had had nine of her crew killed and three wounded. He did not know that, with her wheelhouse badly hit, it was necessary for her to steer from aft, a difficult operation in the twisting and forceful current of the Yangtse.

"Perhaps," Weston said. He felt very tired.

Nobody looked hopeful.

The Communist guns, though quiet now, were still there, mounting a grim guard. Every one in the ship was conscious of the threat they offered. The frigate was still stuck in the mud. Officers and men alike felt dispirited, prodded by the subconscious, unreasonable reminder that they had had a chance to escape and had failed to do so.

Berger rested on a stretcher on the floor of the wireless-room now, trying not to think of the ever-present pain. He said very little. He was ill and weak, spent by loss of blood and by his unrelenting activity during the shelling.

After a while Weston remembered that he had not eaten since breakfast. He tried to eat, but he couldn't seem to keep anything down. He tried to drink water, but even that was impossible. Finally he said, "Will somebody get me a horse's neck?"

A horse's neck is a favourite Navy drink, made of brandy and ginger-ale. Weston sipped at it gratefully. It stayed down. For several days he could swallow no other form of nourishment.

There were new and urgent problems to be faced. Many of the wounded still on board had become delirious. They were moaning with the pain and asking for help. By now, unfortunately, all the tubonic ampules of morphia on board had become exhausted. There was, it is true, a further supply of morphia on the ship, but it was in a different form, and, with the doctor dead, no one knew if it was safe to use or if it might prove fatal.

As Weston wrote later in his official report to the Admiralty, "It was erroneously supposed that a patient who had been receiving a morphine chloride preparation could not be given later a sulphate preparation when the former ran out."

Strain, who, as the flotilla electrical officer, was not a member of *Amethyst's* company—he had been taken on board at Shanghai as a passenger for Nanking—had during the afternoon managed to repair the wireless-set.

French tapped out an urgent signal requesting delivery of tubonic ampules of morphia.

At about five o'clock that afternoon Hett asked Griffiths, "Do you think you can organize a meal for the ship's company?"

"I'll do the best I can, sir."

Griffiths went to see McNamara in the N.A.A.F.I. canteen. From him he collected some tinned soup. Then he drew pickles from McCarthy, the stores petty officer. He cut up the cold beef which he had cooked, but had not served for the midday meal, and boiled enough potatoes to go round. Tea and bread and butter completed the menu.

They had eaten no midday meal, but even so, the men ate with very little appetite.

During the evening an incident occurred which deepened the gloom. Daylight was fading when Weston, with a great effort of will, managed to get out of his chair and on to his feet. The pain in his chest had spread. It burned and throbbed, and the pain had sapped his strength.

"Give me a hand, will you?" he asked Wilfrid Parnell. The boy jumped to his side.

Weston rested his right arm across Parnell's shoulders and, with a stick in his left hand, hobbled down to the after messdeck to see how *Amethyst's* badly wounded captain was faring.

There was nothing Weston could do to help.

Near Skinner one of the Chinese river pilots was moaning and whimpering. When he saw Weston he gave an agonized scream. His face was distorted with pain.

"Shoot me!" he begged Weston. "Shoot me, please!"

The back of his head had been peeled off by a shell-splinter. Weston shook his head in a firm but sympathetic negative.

"Please!" the pilot repeated. He could see that Weston would not shoot him.

The Chinese stuffed his right hand into his mouth with great force. Then he tried it again.

"He's been doing that all the afternoon," Hett said, shaking his head.

"Poor bastard!" somebody remarked. "He's going crazy with the pain, and there's nothing we can do about it."

Weston said, "No. He's trying to commit suicide. He's trying to stuff his tongue down his throat and choke himself to death with it. Poor blighter!" In fact, this was an ancient Chinese method of committing suicide when no weapon was at hand with which to do the job.

Weston hobbled around, still leaning on Parnell, to see the other Chinese pilot, who was unhurt. "Your friend is badly wounded," he told him. "That means we have only you to show us the channel if we get off the mud. Don't, under any circumstances, leave the ship."

The pilot nodded unhappily. He didn't seem to care much for his new responsibility.

At six o'clock, with dusk approaching, Hett stood at the ship's rail on the shoreward side.

"Hello!" he shouted. "Shore party, hello!"

From the deep grass somebody replied. "Hello, *Amethyst*!"

"What's the situation there?"

"The Chinese are friendly; but there are mines about, and we don't like to move."

"How many are you?"

There was a pause for a quick consultation. Then: "Fifteen." These were mostly stragglers who had managed to get ashore on Carley floats and by swimming, but who had been swept down by the current and had collected together later, long after Heath and the other parties had crossed over to the mainland. The various parts and sections of this first chaotic evacuation will probably never be sorted out.

Hett said, "Right. Monaghan will be going ashore in the whaler to try and locate a Chinese doctor and get medical supplies for the wounded. Wait right where you are. He'll bring you back out to the ship when he returns."

Monaghan did not know that Weston had ordered the second Chinese pilot to remain on board. He climbed into the whaler through an escape hatch which opened off the petty officers' mess-deck. With him he took as interpreters the ship's tailor (one of the eight Chinese attached to *Amethyst*) and the second pilot. He took both, since they spoke different dialects and there was no telling which might be the more useful. The pilot spoke a Northern Chinese dialect, and the tailor spoke Cantonese.

It was not until they climbed out of the whaler and scrambled up the steep bank that Hett, still at the ship's rail, noticed the pilot. He was carrying a leather gladstone-bag.

"Hey, Guns!" Hett shouted anxiously to Monaghan.

"Yes?" The commissioned gunner turned. He was a hundred yards or more away, and a light breeze made it difficult to hear.

"Make sure the pilot comes back. He's got his bag with him."

When the whaler returned, some time later, the pilot was not in it.

Monaghan explained. "He's coming back at eight o'clock with the Chinese doctor." At eight, however, the pilot had not returned. At nine he was still missing. *Amethyst* never saw him again.

No one on board dared voice the cliché about rats deserting a sinking ship. It was too close to the bone. Now if *Amethyst* got off the mud and could run for it she would have to take her chances with the changing, treacherous channel.

She would have to take the river at high speed without a pilot experienced in its shifting ways.

Chapter Eight

JOURNEY

Not more than a quarter of an hour after Bannister and Martin had been put down on their stretchers on the floor of the hut four Chinese coolies entered. Their flat, yellow faces were quite impassive. Two of them lifted Bannister's stretcher, without jarring Bannister at all, and looped the handles through yokes resting on their shoulders. The remaining pair did the same with Martin. They carried the wounded sailors down a narrow lane of the village.

"Hey!" Bannister protested. "Where are you taking us?" He couldn't see if Heath and the others were following behind. The bearers, who understood no English, remained silent. They carried the wounded youths stolidly along.

Bannister still had a hard time breathing. There was a constant gurgling in his throat, and it worried him. It sounded almost like a rattle of death. He fought for breath and against the pain, and against a rising fear that he and Martin were being separated from the rest of the *Amethyst* party of evacuees.

Martin and he were carried along for ten minutes. Then they were lowered gently to the ground in front of a small stone cottage with a thatched roof.

One of the coolies brought out a packet of Chinese-made cigarettes. He put two of them into his mouth. He lit them carefully, protecting his match from the wind with cupped hands, and put one between Bannister's lips.

"Thank you," Bannister said. The cigarette did seem to help.

After a five-minute rest the coolies lifted the stretchers on to their shoulders and loped off again. They moved very quickly, but nevertheless managed to get along quite smoothly at the same time, obviously taking care to do so, as if they were trying very hard to save Bannister and Martin from being shaken more than was absolutely necessary.

A crowd of villagers had collected along both sides of the lane to witness the awkward little procession. The women wore long, plain black dresses, the skirts of which reached down to mid-calf and were slit on one side. The younger men wore cheap, European-style suits, but their elders were dressed in long priest-like gowns. Their wide, Oriental faces gaped silently as the stretchers were carried along the lane.

The bearers soon left the village behind. They made their way along the path, zig-zagging through the rice-paddies. Then they cut into another path, just as narrow and tortuous, branching off to the left. Bannister managed to twist his head, with a new spasm of pain, far enough to see, with a tremendous feeling of relief, that Heath and the others were marching along behind them. For a while after that his wound seemed to hurt a little less.

They came to Fang-lo-ching, another small and poverty-stricken village, and Bannister and Martin were carried through the narrow, cobbled main street. The population of Fang-lo-ching had been quadrupled by incoming refugees from the north side of the Yangtse. These refugees sat dejectedly around in the street, boiling rice over open fires, which smelled sharply of burning bamboo. The bearers stopped at the central square and put the stretchers down.

There were now more than sixty evacuees in Heath's party. They assembled together in the central square of Fang-lo-ching. Bannister and Martin were carried into a small wooden shed. A party of Nationalist soldiers made beds for them by placing wooden doors across wooden boxes and covering the doors with straw.

The two wounded sailors rested there silently. In spite of the care their bearers had taken, the journey thus far had weakened them considerably. Presently two of their ship-mates, Leading Seaman Mullins and Signalman David Thomas, came in for a visit. Thomas had one arm in a sling.

"I s'pose you're wondering what's been happening, Paddy?" Mullins asked Bannister.

"Yes, I am."

"We're trying to get to Shanghai. We're trying to get a couple of lorries sent down from Shanghai to pick us up, see? How do you feel?"

"I can't breathe, like."

Mullins held a thumb up. "Aw, you'll be okay, Paddy." He felt embarrassed talking to the wounded man, thinking that it might just as easily have been him lying there on the stretcher. He shifted uncomfortably from one foot to the other. Then he and Thomas returned to their mates in the town square.

A little later Martin was moved to another small room in the shed. Bannister was quite alone. He let his thoughts wander, first home to Belfast, then to the ship. He wondered if he would ever get to Shanghai. Although he had not eaten since breakfast—it now seemed many days since he had seen that first shell splash into the water of the Yangtse near the ship, though it was only six and a half hours earlier—he did not think of food. It was now three o'clock in the afternoon. He listened to the gurgling sound of his breathing for a while, worrying about it, but refusing to panic, and then he thought of nothing at all.

After a little more than an hour of solitude two Chinese civilians entered and carried his stretcher out to where the others were resting around the square. Some were quietly sitting on the rough, stone steps of the houses; some were standing, loosely and uncomfortably; others sat on the bare ground. Most of *Amethyst's* men looked haggard and worried. Presently Martin was brought out and put on the ground near Bannister.

Canning came over to talk to Bannister.

"You all right, mate?" Canning's face expressed his deep concern.

"Sure, Lofty, I think so. Have you seen Brownie and Muldoon?" Bannister had known Brown, Muldoon, and Canning for a long time. The four had been in barracks together at Devonport.

"No, mate, I haven't."

Neither knew that Muldoon had been killed shortly after Bannister had left the ship in that first shoreward trip of the whaler.

None of the party had any idea of what had happened to *Amethyst*; but each man wondered and worried about the friends he had left behind, and hoped, with no great confidence, for the best.

At half-past six, in the deepening dusk, Bannister and Martin were lifted again on to the shoulders of their bearers. They were carried out of Fang-lo-ching along narrow lanes which soon were sentinelled on either side by overhanging trees. To Bannister in the gloom it seemed as if they were passing through a thick and menacing jungle. Overhead, against the dull sky and between the pattern of crossed branches, he could see bats darting and dodging, making incredible hairpin turns and seeming somehow rather wicked. Thousands of insects buzzed by.

Some time later they came to a group of buildings which looked, by the way they loomed up in the dark, like large barns. Nationalist soldiers occupied some of these barnlike buildings, and their paraffin-oil lamps lent the yawning interiors a certain reluctant cheerfulness. Bannister was carried into a barn which had no lamp. He could see nothing. When his bearers left him he did not know if he was alone or if he had company in the barn.

His wound began to throb. He shifted on his stretcher, trying to make himself more comfortable, thinking that perhaps in another position the pain would be less intense; and as he moved he rolled off the stretcher on to the hard mud floor. He squirmed on the mud, trying frantically to get back on to the stretcher. The wheezing and gurgling became louder. He was very weak by now, and he couldn't manage it.

The struggle had irritated his wound, and the pain was now almost unbearable.

"Will somebody please help me back on my stretcher ain?"

He thought he had shouted the request, but it came out a plaintive croak in his Belfast brogue. Nobody heard him.

For a while Bannister mercifully slipped into unconsciousness. When he regained his senses he found himself once again in a world surrounded by pain, and almost at once lost consciousness again. The night went like that. Sometimes he was alive and wished he were not; sometimes he was quite oblivious to reality.

At daybreak a group of Nationalist soldiers entered the barn, chattering cheerfully. Bannister had never seen them before. He was afraid.

The soldiers put him back on his stretcher, making little clucking sounds of concern. The sounds were no comfort to him. Bannister looked round the barn, which was now quite light, for his shipmates, but there was none in sight. The fear rose quickly in him, quickly and out of control. "Have they left me behind?" he thought. "Am I alone?"

The soldiers carried him out of the barn and into a small wooden hut. Martin was in the hut, lying on his stretcher. He grinned at Bannister.

"Gosh, am I glad to see you!" Martin said.

Bannister sighed gratefully. It came out a thick gurgle. "Where are the others?"

"I don't know."

"They must be off getting the lorries for us, like."

"Sure," Martin said. He sounded uncertain.

The two wounded youths were carried off again on their stretchers. They were becoming accustomed to the easy swing of being carried that way. The Chinese bearers were very good at the job.

But Martin was anxious. "Hey!" he shouted, a little wildly. "How'll our mates know where we are?"

The bearers said nothing.

By now both Bannister and Martin were completely confused. "Where are these Chinese blokes taking us?" Bannister thought, over and over again. One thing was becoming quite clear: he and Martin had now definitely become separated from the main body of *Amethyst* evacuees.

Chapter Nine

UNSTUCK

When Wilkinson, the engineer officer, returned to *Amethyst* in the whaler with Monaghan that first evening he had a talk with Weston. Then he climbed down to the engineroom and ordered the boilers to be flashed up and a head of steam to be raised. It takes time to raise steam, and it was half-past ten before there was sufficient pressure.

"All set," Wilkinson shouted up the voice-pipe.

"Right," Weston said. He had less difficulty with his breathing now, and could easily be understood: he no longer mangled his words. "Full astern, both engines!" he ordered. He waited tensely.

Both engines were put full astern. The screws, free of the mud, churned the water at *Amethyst's* stern until it became opaque. The ship did not budge.

Wilkinson tried desperate variations with his twin power-plants. The port engine was driven full astern; the starboard engine full ahead in an effort to wriggle off the mudbank, since a straight backward pull would not do the trick. Then the starboard engine was tried full astern with the port engine full ahead.

It was no use. The mud's sucking grip was as firm and solid as ever.

Up above Weston stubbornly refused to give up the attempt. "All right," he said. "We'll just have to lighten ship." Down the voice-pipe he said to Wilkinson, "Hold it, Chief, for further orders."

Wilkinson and Williams and the rest of the engineroom crew waited down below.

Meanwhile Weston got a party at work on the upper deck.

Anything that was loose and heavy and could be spared was thrown over the side—awning stanchions, kedge anchor, steel derricks, all splashed into the Yangtse and plunged to the soft bottom. At the same time Weston ordered fuel-oil to be pumped over the side from the forward tanks in order to give added buoyancy to the bows. A thick scum of oil spread over the dark surface of the river and was carried downstream by the current.

At midnight Berger, who had had himself carried up to the bridge, rang down to the engineroom. "Chief," he said, "we're going to have another try." He had lost considerable blood, and was working largely on his nerves. His voice sounded weary, but hopeful.

Wilkinson was unaware of the previous upperdeck activity, and did not share Berger's optimism. He did not expect anything more than a repetition of the earlier failure. "Right," he said grimly. At least, he was determined to try.

He employed the same tactics he had used before—one engine full astern, the other full ahead; then both engines together full astern.

At first nothing. Then, a few minutes later, the elated buzz came down from the bridge: "We're moving, Chief! Keep at it! We're moving!"

Amethyst had indeed reluctantly begun to move.

Chapter Ten

THE LETTER

At ten o'clock on the morning of the 21st of April Lieutenant-Commander John Simon Kerans, a slender, intense man in his mid-thirties, left Nanking. Kerans was of above average height; his face was long and lean and handsome, with a straight, almost Grecian nose, a smallish mouth, and very small ears that were pinned close to his head. He had been born in Birr, County Offaly, but there was now no trace of brogue in his English-sounding voice. His ultimate destination, although he was far from certain then that he would reach her, was the frigate *Amethyst*.

He went by jeep, and was accompanied by the British Embassy's Assistant Military Attaché, Lieutenant-Colonel R. V. Dewar-Durie. In the jeep he carried medical supplies—including morphia—a case of beer, two thousand cigarettes, and a Chinese Admiralty chart folio of the Yangtse. A signal had come up from *Amethyst* advising Nanking that some of her charts had been destroyed in the shelling, and Kerans, acting on his own initiative, had decided to take the new set with him.

The jeep, which Kerans considered to be the most reliable one available to him in Nanking, had been lent to him by the Australian Military Attaché, a Colonel Clark. The Navy jeep, an unreliable vehicle which had seen better days, and which seemed to spend most of its time being taken apart and put together again, had been in the garage, as usual, for repairs. Kerans had no confidence in its ability to stand the rugged journey, and it was a great relief to him to get the use of the Australian car.

Even so, he had many delays on the way down. Some were

caused by engine-trouble, which came in turn from the poor-quality petrol. In addition, the roads were exceedingly uninviting. The miles stretched out, loosely packed with rubble in places, deeply rutted in others. There were many detours, some of them mere bullock-tracks never intended for the passage of motor vehicles.

The road twisted and turned. It was narrow and dusty. The jeep churned up the dust into a following cloud, and the dust settled down on Kerans and Dewar-Durie, coating their faces and hands and clothing, creeping drily up their nostrils, getting into their eyes.

Crowds of peasants made their slow, awkward way along the road on foot, hesitating dumbly, like cattle, when the jeep came along, and blocking the way in spite of Kerans' urgent honking of the horn. After a while the horn broke down.

Presently Kerans came upon a platoon of Nationalist infantry slogging stubbornly along in the middle of the narrow road. There was no room for him to pass them in the jeep. He slowed down. The soldiers continued to march down the road, ignoring the jeep on their tail. Kerans jabbed at the horn. It made no sound.

"Hoy!" he cried. "Hoy! Hoy!" Then, forgetting himself for a moment: "Get the hell off the road and let me pass!"

After a while the Chinese soldiers got the idea. They moved over to the verges, and Kerans roared by, trailing a billowing cloud of dust.

In places the road was so bad that Kerans had to slow down to bottom gear and make his way gingerly along the deeply gouged ruts.

"It's lucky it isn't the rainy season, D.D.," he said. "We'd be over our wheels in mud."

Dewar-Durie nodded, saying nothing. His throat was dry with the coating of dust.

The seventy-two miles from Nanking to Chingkiang took just over three and a half hours. By the time they reached Chingkiang the two officers felt stiff and sore and tired.

*Hauling up the
Oil by Davit*

*The Side-party
Sampan*

Commander J. S. Kerans, D.S.O., then a Lieutenant-Commander

"A man who can survive this," Dewar-Durie remarked, "can survive anything."

Before he had left Nanking Kerans had taken the precaution of calling on the Commander-in-Chief of the Chinese Nationalist Navy, Admiral Kwei Yung Ching. Now he carried a letter of authority in his pocket.

It read in Chinese:

> This is to certify that Lieutenant-Commander Kerans is proceeding on a tour of investigation along the river in connexion with the shelling of the British warship by the bandits. All our warships along the river, and our land organization, are hereby requested to provide him facilities.

It was signed by the Admiral.

At Chingkiang Kerans' first call was on the Nationalist Naval Chief of Staff, a short, pleasant little man who had been trained in the United States and spoke excellent English.

"I understand," Kerans said to him, after formal greetings, "that there are twenty British naval ratings in hospital here."

Kerans had been told this in Nanking.

"I'm sorry"—the Chinese officer smiled apologetically—"but this is not so."

Kerans was puzzled by this development. "Are you sure?"

"Quite sure. I would be the first to know of such a thing." He soon convinced the Lieutenant-Commander that a mistake had been made.

"All right, then," Kerans said. "Can you help me get my medical supplies to *Amethyst*? Can you take me to the ship in one of your naval craft?"

The mobile face of the little Chinese was heavy with regret. "So sorry," he said. "All our naval craft have been damaged, except for a few which are far too slow for the undertaking."

Kerans tried to persuade him to change his mind, but he was unable to do so. "May I telephone Nanking?" Kerans asked finally.

"Of course."

Kerans 'phoned Captain Donaldson, the Naval Attaché to the Embassy. He explained the situation in detail.

E

Donaldson said, "Too bad. At any rate, a U.S. naval doctor has been lent to us. He's coming down there with more medical supplies. Perhaps he can give you a hand."

The Nationalist naval headquarters in Chingkiang was a large, solidly built, two-storey Western-style house near the waterfront. Chingkiang itself was a walled city, once a flourishing treaty port, but now suffering from decay. It was on the south bank of the Yangtse. Kerans waited in a large, sparsely furnished room. There was nothing he could do for a while. He was very tired after the rough trip down from Nanking. He sat down on a hard bench beside Dewar-Durie. The two slouched, side by side, in silent dejection.

After a while a Chinese sub-lieutenant came into the room. He was about twenty-two, but he looked younger than that. His uniform, very similar to the British naval uniform, needed pressing. When he saw Kerans his white teeth gleamed in a broad welcoming grin. He came over to him.

"You are the British officer?"

"Yes."

"Ah! I have some information for you."

"You mean about *Amethyst*?" Kerans was all interest.

"Yes. I was alongside her this morning in a landing-craft. I asked if I could take away the wounded, but the Captain said no."

"I see," Kerans said. It was good to get even the flimsiest of second-hand news of the ship. Somehow it seemed to bring his mission closer to success. "I have medical supplies. Could you take me back to *Amethyst* with you?"

The sub-lieutenant's grin faded. He shook his head. "Our craft are much too slow. I was under fire on the way back this morning, and was lucky to escape."

At three that afternoon Kerans telephoned Donaldson again.

"I can't get out to *Amethyst*," he reported. "Fact is, there's nothing further I can do here. I'll be returning shortly. Is that all right with you?"

Now he felt, unhappily, that his mission had failed.

"Okay," Donaldson said. "Come on back."

Chapter Eleven

SAFETY FOR SOME

When Heath returned to the hut after watching *Consort* disappear down-river that first afternoon he asked the Chinese Major to provide stretcher-bearers for Martin and Bannister. Martin, who had been walking with the other less seriously wounded, even with the deep gash in his left thigh, had suddenly collapsed.

Heath and the other swimmers had been given clothes by the Chinese, but those who had discarded their shoes were still barefoot.

The stretcher-bearers led the way across the paddy-fields. The rest of the party stretched out in an incredibly long, thin line behind them. Heath brought up the rear. The bearers moved at an almost unbelievable speed with their heavy loads. "At times," Heath reported later, "we had to trot to keep up with them along the narrow path." They waded across small streams and wound through paddy-fields and up hill and down.

At half-past nine, after a march of twenty miles, the party arrived at a large village. Some of the shoeless men had bleeding feet. All were exhausted. It had grown bitterly cold with the setting of the sun.

They rested for three hours at the village, making the most of it. At half-past twelve in the new-born morning of the 21st of April a small steam motor-boat chugged in to take the party across the Hsiao-ho Creek to the main road for Shanghai. A Chinese medical orderly said, "You no take wounded."

"Of course I'll be taking the wounded," Heath retorted with some indignation. He had kept his party together thus far; he was not going to lose any of his charges now.

"Not those two men," the orderly insisted gravely. He waved an arm towards the barn and the hut where Bannister and Martin had been put. "Won't stand journey." He shook his head with slow solemnity.

There was very little time for Heath to make his decision. "The medical bloke ought to know," he reflected doubtfully.

"All right," he said. "I'll leave them here for the night and send back for them to-morrow."

At the other side of the creek three American-made lorries awaited them. Heath had the half-dozen wounded loaded on to one of the lorries. The others piled into the remaining two. Then they sped down the rough roads at fifty miles an hour. They reached Changchow, a large town, at four in the morning. It was pitch-black. Heath was met by a Major Li, who spoke perfect English.

"What can I do for you and your men?" the Major asked.

"Can we get the wounded to hospital?"

The Major said that it could be arranged. Then Heath asked his advice about what to do regarding Bannister and Martin.

"We'll get them up here to the hospital," the Major promised. "As soon as they're fit to travel we'll send them on to Shanghai."

Heath felt that the two wounded youths would be in good hands.

That night Heath's party of evacuees slept between sheets, three men to a bed, in the two local hotels. They were exhausted and slept soundly. Next day Heath was escorted to the Nationalist Army Headquarters, and was granted an interview with Lieutenant-General Pai, the area commander for Kiangsu Province. The General was pleasant and eager to help. He agreed to provide a railway carriage to take the large party on their way.

Heath and his men reached Shanghai without further trouble. This was the first party of *Amethyst* evacuees to reach safety.

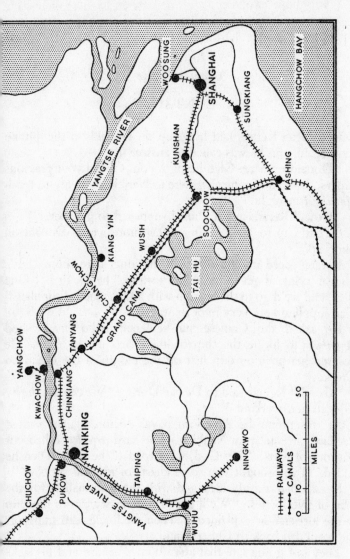

THE LOWER REACHES OF THE YANGTSE

Chapter Twelve

CONTACT

Shortly after Kerans had hung up on Donaldson the 'phone rang again, and he was called to answer it.

"Donaldson here. Glad I caught you. Cancel your previous orders. Instead of returning here to Nanking you are to reach *Amethyst* to-night."

"How," Kerans asked, "am I supposed to get there?"

"That's up to you." After a few more words Donaldson hung up.

Kerans paced up and down in the long, bare room. "It's no use trying to get to the ship by water," he decided. "One shell, and we'd go to the bottom with all the medical supplies." The supplies were very important.

He asked the Chinese sub-lieutenant who had visited *Amethyst* to locate the ship on his charts of the river. He pointed her position out, just off the mouth of the Hsiao-ho Creek.

"Good," Kerans said to Dewar-Durie. "We can get pretty close to her overland."

At this point the American naval doctor, a man named Packard, arrived from Nanking. The hard trip down had put him out of sorts. "My God, what roads!" he said. Then he added, "I've brought you some chests of medical supplies."

Kerans had already arranged with the Nationalists for the loan of two lorries. "We'll get as close as we can to the ship in the lorries," he explained. "Then the lorries can transport the wounded back to Chingkiang."

They got going late that afternoon. Packard and his sick-bay attendant and the Chinese Naval Chief of Staff went with them. The road along the river had been constructed not long previously for emergency military use. It was merely a rough, rutted track, far worse than the road Heath and his party had taken to Changchow, or even than the detour-ridden road from Nanking to Chingkiang. The lorries crawled along it at five miles an hour, with their motors growling in low gear. At Tachiang the road tailed out into nothing.

Tachiang is a tiny farming village, very poor and smelling strongly of the barnyard. It consists of a few mud huts and little else. Kerans hopped out of his lorry. He arranged with some of the villagers to act as stretcher-bearers to bring out the wounded and for coolies to carry the chests of medical supplies in to the ship.

The coolies, grunting a little with the weight of the chests, loaded them on two peculiarly Chinese wheel-barrows, distinguished by the single four-feet-high wheel on which each was rolled. There were three coolies to each barrow, one pushing on each of the two wooden arms and one pulling on a rope harness in front of the big wheel.

The strange procession started out along the single-file pathway at six o'clock, twisting through the rice-fields as daylight began to fade. It consisted of ten Chinese coolies, half a dozen Nationalist soldiers as escort, Packard and his assistant, the Chinese naval officer, Dewar-Durie, Kerans, and the two giant-wheeled barrows squeaking a repetitive protest.

Kerans was tired before he began the hike. He had had a hard and exhausting day, trying on the nerves as well as the body. Very soon he began to shiver in the chill of the early spring evening. It had been quite warm during the day, and he had worn no greatcoat; but with the setting of the sun the temperature had dropped to a point near freezing. Kerans plodded on.

The procession passed through tiny mud villages, each one anachronistically surrounded by a brick wall. It grew darker and colder. Kerans moved his arms briskly, trying to generate some warmth. Stray dogs barked and growled and howled in the distance; but the peasants, knowing the war was on their very doorstep, had locked themselves in for the night. There was no electricity, but now and then Kerans could see the faint flickering light from home-made tallow candles through the chinks of the boarded-up windows. He was getting to be ravenously hungry. He had brought nothing to eat with him, and silently cursed his carelessness and lack of foresight. He must, presently, have mumbled something aloud.

"What's your trouble?" Packard asked. "Hungry?" The American had been following along behind Kerans in the long, hotch-potch single file.

"Dammit, yes. I haven't eaten since breakfast."

The American cluck-clucked with his tongue. "You must be starved. Look; I grabbed some emergency rations when I left Nanking. Turned out to be tinned plum-pudding and tinned cheese. Horrible combination, but nourishing enough. You're welcome to some when we stop."

"Thanks. By then I'll be ready to eat anything. I am now."

At about ten that night they came to the shore of a dark creek. Their Chinese guides had told Kerans that that was where *Amethyst* would be. The ship was not in sight.

"Obviously somebody has made a mistake," the Chinese Naval Chief of Staff said querulously. "I'll ask the people in this hut if they've heard anything about your ship." There was a wood-and-mud hut on the bank of the creek. Candlelight showed through the cracks. The Chinese officer knocked at the door and spoke in nasal sing-song to a fisherman who came to answer. Another fisherman edged curiously forward into the doorway, and another. The Chinese officer sighed impatiently.

Over his shoulder he said to Kerans, "They don't know a thing. Not a thing! I'm going to hike back to that last village and check up. You and the doctor and the Colonel had better wait inside this hut until you hear from me." The last village they had passed through was a good four miles behind them, through the paddy-fields. Muttering unhappily to himself, and taking two coolies with him as runners, the Nationalist sailor left.

Packard, Dewar-Durie, and Kerans entered the hut. Dewar-Durie screwed his face into a grimace.

"Phew!" he said. The hut smelled of decay.

Three fishermen and their two women watched them silently from the far side of the room, deliberately keeping apart, probably through shyness. In spite of the objectionable smell, the hut was warm. The warmth was a relief from the bitterly chill out-of-doors.

"Might as well try some of this grub," Packard said. He took some tins out of his knapsack. He opened the tins, and they ate the cold plum-pudding and the cheese.

"It tastes fine to me," Kerans said. He was glad to put anything into his empty stomach.

Some time later one of the runners came back from the village with a message. It said that they would have to walk back to the village and set off in another direction from there.

They walked wearily back. Kerans arranged with the headman of the village to provide food for the coolies, and the procession set out once again.

It was very dark. Presently five of the coolie bearers refused to go on; they explained that they did not like putting so much distance between themselves and their own village. Kerans and his party continued with the other coolies.

Just at midnight Kerans saw what looked like the quick flash of an electric torch not far ahead. Then he heard an outlandish jumble of sound. As he came closer to the sound he realized that it was a large group of Chinese civilians, chattering in their sing-song tongue. Near them he once again saw the flash of an electric torch.

Out of the darkness somebody spoke.

"Are you a naval officer, sir?"

It was a British naval rating.

Chapter Thirteen

THE MESSAGE

On board *Amethyst*, at about eight o'clock on the evening of the 20th, Hett had asked for volunteers who would gather the dead together, removing them from where they had fallen at the time of the action to X-gun deck.

"Me, sir," McNamara, the canteen manager, said.

"Me, sir," George Hartness and Leighton Rees echoed.

It was pitch-dark, and because of Communist snipers they could use no light. McNamara felt his way along the upper deck until he came to a body. He groped along the thigh and along the side of the torso, and before he could stop his hand slid all the way into a wet and gaping wound. For a moment he felt sure that he was going to vomit.

Then he went back to speak to Hett.

"It's no good trying to do this in the dark, sir," he said. He still felt ill. "We would do more harm than good."

Hett saw that McNamara's face was quite without colour. "Right," he said. "Tackle it in the morning, then."

Early on Thursday, after the ship backed off the mud, she moved about a mile and a half up-river and dropped anchor.

"Okay," Wilkinson told Williams. "Now we can shut the steam off the main engines." Like every man of the ship's company, he was quite exhausted. He set up a camp-bed in the engineroom, where he would be ready in case of emergency, and tried to get some sleep. Everybody needed it.

Weston sat down again in the canvas-bottomed chair in the wireless office. He propped his head on a suitcase resting on the desk in front of him and dozed off. French was beside him, at the key.

74

Hett awoke before dawn, after he had had only an hour's sleep, feeling uneasily aware that there was something calling for his attention. He had no idea what it could be. He went out on deck and looked round. Then he noticed that several black and shining objects were bobbing up and down in the water, on all sides of the ship. "Mines!" he thought. Then, as the sun rose, he was able to see that the menacing black objects were not mines after all, but only glass fishing-floats. He laughed silently, feeling better at once.

A little later McNamara, Rees, and Albert Garns—Hartness was needed elsewhere, and Garns had volunteered to substitute for him—set to work at their grim task of collecting the dead together.

Garns went out on the upper deck through the captain's hatch, crouching low. He was afraid of the snipers on the far shore. He stumbled over the body of one of the ammunition numbers. Garns tried to lift the body without any assistance, and as he did so a groan seemed to leave the dead man's mouth. Garns almost dropped the body.

"He's alive!" he thought. But the body was quite stiff, and the man had been dead for some time. The sun was quite warm now, and getting warmer, and the corpses were beginning to throw off the sweet, unwelcome, sickly smell of death. Monaghan brought up a bottle of whisky from the wardroom.

"Better have a tot of this," he said.

Each of the three men had a long drink. Then they went back to collecting the dead. The bodies which were still in one piece were carried down to X-gun deck by the arms and legs. The others were rolled into hammocks and carried that way.

The men had another tot of whisky. Then the job was done. The bodies were spread neatly round X-gun deck, covered with hammocks and blankets.

It had not been an easy job to do.

Weston felt almost himself again when he awoke that

morning. He was delighted to discover that he could move about the ship without Parnell's help.

At ten o'clock French, who had had no sleep since the action, picked up a signal which lent *Amethyst* fresh hope. The signal announced that *London*, a cruiser, and *Black Swan*, another frigate, were on their way up-river to help them if they could. The rescue-ships were scheduled to arrive at about eleven o'clock.

The men were elated as the news raced round the ship. They knew that a rescue would almost surely mean another brush with the Communist guns; but, at least, now they would eventually get out to the open sea and rejoin the fleet. They had no doubt that this time the rescue attempt would succeed, and they whistled and hummed and cracked edgy jokes at one another.

Shortly after the signal was received a Nationalist officer came alongside in a small boat and boarded the ship. "We've come to take your wounded to hospital in Chingkiang," he told Weston.

Weston, anticipating H.M.S. *London's* arrival in about half an hour, shook his head. "Thank you," he said, "but we don't intend to land any more of our wounded unless it is definitely decided that we're not going down-river." He did not mention *London's* expected appearance on the scene.

The Chinese officer saluted and left.

At five minutes to eleven *Amethyst* got under way. Excitement on board was feverish. Weston and Hett stood on the bridge, their eyes peeled for the first sight of *London*. *Amethyst* circled round in the river. The Communists fired a warning shot, however, and she dropped anchor, while still remaining on the alert to lift it once more and head at full speed for the distant sea.

At eleven the deep, distant roll of artillery carried up from down-river.

"*London*?" Hett asked anxiously.

"Hope so," Weston replied. They stood there, tensely waiting.

At a quarter past twelve, French, still on duty in the wireless office, received a message from H.M.S. *London:*

AM SORRY WE CANNOT HELP YOU TO-DAY. WE SHALL KEEP ON TRYING.

Gloom descended over *Amethyst* again.

Chapter Fourteen

THE HOSPITAL

From early morning on April the 21st until four that afternoon Bannister and Martin were carried on their stretchers by Chinese bearers. They had no idea where they were being taken or whether or not they were in good hands. Between them and the Chinese was the impassable barrier of language.

At four they were carried into a small stone house and placed in separate rooms. Presently two lads dressed in Nationalist uniforms—they could not have been older than twelve—came in to see Bannister. They gave him a cigarette and pressed small pink-and-white frosted cakes into his hands.

Bannister tried to eat one of the cakes, but after the first tentative nibble he knew that he would not be able to get it down. He was surprised at the youthfulness of the Chinese soldiers. "They're just babies," he thought. Bannister was only twenty-one.

The Chinese boy soldiers seemed disappointed at Bannister's neglect of the cakes. They looked at one another and exchanged a few rapid words in Chinese, and one of them ran out of the room, returning a moment later carrying two eggs. He held them up, one in each hand, between thumb and forefinger. He smiled at Bannister, as if inviting him to eat the eggs.

Bannister nodded. He was very fond of eggs.

The Chinese boy gave them to him, and made eager signs for Bannister to eat the eggs raw by sucking at them. Bannister shook his head.

"No, no," he said. The two lads seemed puzzled.

Then one of them lit a match for Bannister's cigarette. Bannister took the match. He held it under one of the eggs to show that he wanted to have it cooked. The two boys grinned and chattered eagerly, and the same lad who had brought the eggs ran out with them again. In a few minutes he brought them back. They had been boiled. He gave Bannister a small glazed pottery spoon, and Bannister attacked the eggs and was happy to get them down. The boy who had boiled the eggs looked proud and pleased, and nodded enthusiastically as Bannister ate.

He felt better after that. He indicated that he wished to have paper and pencil, and these were supplied. He drew a warship, a sampan, and a map of the Yangtse. Along the river he marked Nanking, Shanghai, and *Amethyst's* approximate position.

Then, pointing, he tried to make the boys understand that Martin and he should be taken to Nanking or Shanghai or the ship. He was not able to make them understand.

Bannister knew that he and Martin were alone and lost. "Why did the others leave us?" he wondered. He could think of no possible explanation for the apparent desertion. After a while his face became flushed. "Where are we? What's going to happen to us?" He tossed and turned on his stretcher.

After dark that night the two sailors were carried away again, until they came to the shore of what looked, in the dark, to be a quiet lake. Bannister could just see the black, satiny sheen of the water.

Suddenly he heard heavy gunfire. It seemed to come from two directions at once, as if two armies, quite far apart, were shooting at one another with artillery.

There was a large sampan on the shore. The Chinese loaded Bannister and Martin into it. A score of Chinese civilians piled in after them. They moved out from shore, scarcely making a sound. It was very quiet; the shooting had died away. The people in the sampan hardly seemed to breathe. Bannister decided that they must be trying to slip past some armed outpost without being fired upon. In the dark the flat, Chinese faces seemed extraordinarily pale and momentarily expectant of disaster.

When the sampan reached the far shore without incident the

party of civilians scrambled on to the land and made off into the night.

The two *Amethyst* men were carried into a large house. They slept between clean sheets in real beds; but the distant, disturbing roll of gunfire kept waking them up. They talked in nervous whispers from time to time during the night, discussing their chances. The guns were getting nearer.

Next morning Bannister felt much stronger. "I think I'll be able to walk," he said to Martin, quite pleased with himself.

A thirteen-year-old boy in the brown uniform of the Nationalists helped him to his feet. The boy was less than five feet tall and very slight, but his strength was astonishing. Bannister managed to walk without help for a few yards; then he could walk no farther.

The boy smiled confidently, showing his teeth, and placed Bannister's hands on his thin shoulders, and then, hugging his own arms round Bannister's buttocks and lifting him up without apparent effort, carried him the three hundred yards to a waiting lorry. He set him down easily on the road, not breathing any harder than he had been five minutes before.

He helped Bannister into the seat of the lorry, beside the driver and a Chinese Nationalist air-force pilot, who was wearing his brown, American-style uniform. Martin, on his stretcher, was put down in the back of the lorry. A soldier placed a bag of rice under Martin's head as a makeshift pillow.

"Are you okay, mate?' Bannister asked over his shoulder.

"Sure, I'm okay, Paddy."

Two Nationalist soldiers climbed up on the mudguards, standing there and holding on through the open windows of the lorry. Then soldiers and civilians climbed up on the back with Martin, jamming the available space, but leaving Martin plenty of room to breathe.

The road was long and straight, and, by Chinese standards, not bad, but there were still plenty of rough spots. Every time the lorry bumped Bannister cringed with pain. The pilot noticed this after a while, and put one arm round Bannister's shoulder and smiled understandingly at him and held his free

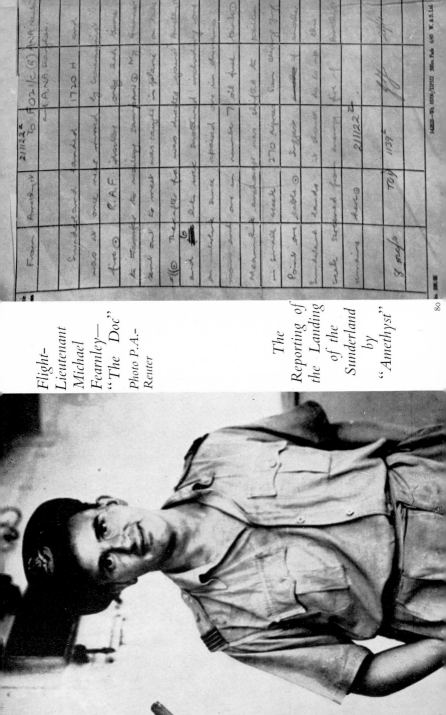

Flight-
Lieutenant
Michael
Fearnley—
"The Doc"

*Photo P.A.-
Reuter*

The
Reporting of
the Landing
of the
Sunderland
by
"Amethyst"

Rutter and French

Photo International News

Griffiths preparing Meat

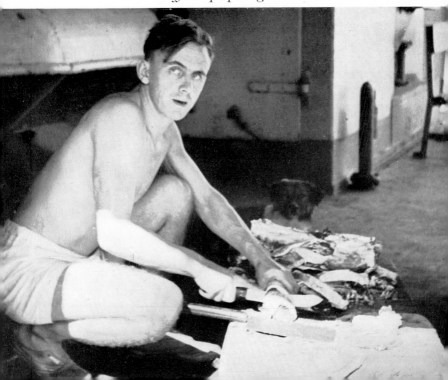

thumb up in a gesture of encouragement. One of the soldiers, the one on Bannister's side, reached in through the window and gave Bannister a cigarette.

After they had been under way for an hour it began to rain. The road was choked with refugees, some of them walking, many leading donkeys piled high with personal belongings, and the rain came down in unbelievably large drops, the size of grapes, perhaps, until soon the refugees were soaked to the skin.

At a small town on the way the driver stopped the lorry and the pilot got out. He went into a house at the roadside, and presently he came out again with a woman, evidently his wife, who brought with her a bowl of boiled water, still warm. She offered it first to Bannister, who drank some of it, and then to Martin, who finished it off. Then the lorry went on its way again, leaving the pilot standing near the house with his wife, waving good-bye to Bannister.

Soon the lorry came to Changchow, where Heath and the first party of evacuees had been, a large town streaming with refugees from the north. The lorry rolled into the walled enclosure of a military barracks and stopped. Bannister and Martin were taken to the American-financed Stevenson Mission Hospital, and were greeted by the Chinese matron, a small woman dressed in a pale-blue Chinese-style gown, long and very simple. She was in her early thirties, and wore her black hair in two buns, one, oddly, over her forehead and the other at the nape of her neck.

"I am Mary Wong," she said. "Four of your *Amethyst* shipmates were here two days ago. I have their names." She pulled a slip of paper out of her pocket and read them off; but neither Bannister nor Martin, both newcomers to *Amethyst*, found any of the names familiar.

The two sailors were assigned a comfortable room, with spick-and-span white walls and two beds.

That same day Bannister was X-rayed. A Chinese doctor, a thin man with serious, dark eyes, said, "We are going to operate on you right away."

F

"Sure," Bannister said. "Go ahead. The quicker you get the splinter out, like, the quicker I'll be able to breathe." By now the right side of his chest had sunk in noticeably, as if his right lung had collapsed.

He was laid out on a white-sheeted operating-table.

"I'm sorry," the doctor said seriously, "but we have no anæsthetic. It will hurt much, but you will feel better when it is done."

"Go ahead," Bannister said. "For God's sake, get it over with," he thought. Perspiration was collecting on his forehead.

The doctor gently pushed Bannister's hands under his buttocks, so that his weight would pin them to the table. Two nurses held his arms down, pressing them tightly against the white sheet for added security. Then the doctor bent down, thin-lipped, and went to work.

He held a shining scalpel in his hand. First he had to enlarge the wound.

Bannister clenched his teeth. He tried very hard to think of distant, happier days at home, but the pain erased everything but itself. The doctor pulled the splinter out of the wound slowly, a fraction of an inch at a time. Once his long, shining tweezers slipped on the fragment of steel, and Bannister's body lifted with the greater spasm of pain.

Then the splinter was out.

The doctor, whose yellow skin was shiny with sweat, held the splinter out triumphantly for Bannister to see. It was about an inch long and half an inch wide, and it was sharp and serrated round the edges.

"There it is." The doctor smiled.

It looked much smaller than Bannister thought it would be. He took a deep, grateful breath. He felt weak and jaded, but very relieved. As he inhaled, the right side of his chest, which had been deflated, seemed to pop out to normal. His right lung had started to work again.

Then the doctor attended Martin's wound in the thigh.

Two days later Mary Wong came round to their room.

Bannister could see that she was unusually pale and nervous. His bed was placed against a window, and he used to amuse himself by looking down into the hospital garden and watching the wounded soldiers being carried in for treatment. That morning he had noted that the wounded were wearing green uniforms, instead of the khaki-brown of the Nationalists.

"The Communists," Mary Wong said, "have captured the town to-day. Eleven thousand of them."

Bannister looked across at Martin.

"That does it," Martin exclaimed.

They each had the same thought: "What will happen to us now?"

Chapter Fifteen

NEW ARRIVAL

About seven hundred and fifty air miles from where *Amethyst* ran into trouble Michael Edward Fearnley, a young doctor serving the last few months of his National Service in the Royal Air Force, went to his room in the Kai Tak officers' mess at Hong Kong. It was late in the afternoon of April the 20th.

Fearnley was of above average height. He had an easy-going temperament, unruly, light-brown hair, and a pleasant face that managed to seem older than his twenty-five years. As soon as he stepped into his room he switched on the radio, to which he did not usually bother to listen. He caught the tail-end of a news flash.

". . . the frigate was fired on at half-past nine by Communist batteries on the Yangtse. . . ."

That was the first he heard of *Amethyst* and her plight, and at the time he was only casually interested.

Shortly before eleven that night he was told by the Air Officer Commanding the Kai Tak station, Group-Captain Jefferson, that an aircraft would be sent to Nanking next day with medical supplies.

"The supplies," Jefferson added, "will be delivered over-land from there. If the plan is carried through you'll be going along, Flight-Lieutenant."

Soon after that Fearnley went to bed. He had a hard time getting the *Amethyst* affair out of his mind, but after a while he dozed off. At three o'clock in the morning a brother-officer awakened him to tell him that the flight was off. He fell into a deep, relieved sleep.

At six he was shaken once again, more vigorously this time. "A Sunderland is leaving for *Amethyst* in half an hour," he was told querulously. "You're going with it. Why aren't you ready?" It was a different officer this time.

Confused over the unexpected change and rechange of plans, and still dopy with sleep, Fearnley had a quick breakfast of bacon and eggs. Then he waited.

There was some delay in the take-off, owing to loading the the aircraft. Jefferson came round to chat. "*Amethyst's* M.O. has been killed," he said. "The idea now is for us to take the medical supplies and land in the river near the ship and transfer the supplies to her. We don't know exactly what the situation is there. Maybe you will go to the ship with the supplies. Maybe you won't. I'm going along in the Sunderland for the ride." It was not then known in Hong Kong how many men were still aboard the ship, how many had landed.

The flying-boat took off at half-past seven, an hour behind schedule. In addition to the crew, Jefferson, Fearnley, and a Navy doctor named Morgan, two experienced Army parachute-droppers were taken along to release supplies over the trapped ship in case a landing proved impossible. It was now known that H.M.S. *London* was on her way up-river to attempt a rescue.

After about five steady hours of flying the Sunderland came to the Yangtse. From five thousand feet the river looked like a huge, sinuous snake with shining, sun-lit scales. Fearnley, looking down through the windows of the flying-boat, found it impossible to tell which way the river flowed. He saw tiny ships on the water, and wondered if one of them was *Amethyst*.

Flight-Lieutenant Ken Letford, the Sunderland's skipper, made his way back to the passenger compartment.

"We've contacted *London*," he announced. His face was long and unhappy. "She's flashed us to proceed to Shanghai, and not attempt a landing. She's come under very heavy fire, and considers we haven't a chance to come in for a landing and transfer the stuff."

The Sunderland detoured to Shanghai. The river there was teeming with junks as the aircraft circled, but, miraculously, a space had been cleared for their landing by the time they hit the water. They touched down at one o'clock in the afternoon.

While the flying-boat refuelled at the B.O.A.C. base Fearnley went to the Palace Hotel, a smart, Western-style building, for lunch. When he returned to the aircraft Letford greeted him with a worried look.

"We've just had a message from *Amethyst*," he told Fearnley. "They need morphia badly." Letford and Jefferson anxiously conferred with Navy officers over a chart of the Yangtse.

On it they found a creek that seemed to be out of range of the Communist battery—at San-chiang-ying, just across the river from Rose Island.

"You could probably find enough water to make a landing on the creek," one of the Navy officers said. He sounded a bit sceptical. "Then, if you made it all right, you could unload your medical supplies and take them overland to the ship."

Jefferson and Letford exchanged a glance and a quick nod.

"We'll want all the daylight we can get," Letford said. "We'll have to take off pretty soon." Shanghai was half an hour's flying-time from Rose Island.

The aircraft took off again at half-past four. During the flight Fearnley and the Navy M.O. hurriedly smashed open the heavy cases of medical supplies. From them they extracted what they thought they'd need—morphia, blood-transfusion sets, bottles of plasma and pentothal, an intravenous anæsthetic. They stuffed these supplies into knapsacks and into their pockets.

When Fearnley returned to the passenger compartment he saw that they were flying over a creek. They followed it for a few moments, flying very low, and suddenly burst out into the wide main river. The flying-boat circled, and beneath him Fearnley for the first time saw *Amethyst*. She was lying close to the south bank. Men waved eagerly at the aircraft from her deck.

One of the Sunderland's crew popped his head out of the forward compartment. He seemed to Fearnley to be a bit flushed. "We're not going to land in the creek after all," he said, "but alongside the ship."

Fearnley nodded in silent agreement. It looked calm and peaceful below them, and he could not believe that the Communists would really start shooting.

At half-past five that afternoon Wilkinson was lying on the deck just outside the wireless office. His head felt thick and heavy, and he was weak from the delayed reaction of shock and loss of blood.

He heard a distant droning, and for a moment thought that he had a strange new buzzing in his head. The droning swelled in volume. He got to his feet with an effort and looked up into the sky, and, after a while, saw a white flying-boat circling above the ship. "What a lovely sight!" he thought absently. For a moment he did not grasp that the Sunderland was in any way connected with *Amethyst's* unhappy position.

Then some of the ship's company ran up from below-decks. They started waving and yelling all about him. Wilkinson's heart began suddenly to pound.

Monaghan had, only a minute before, left the ship in a sampan manned by three coolies. The Chinese stopped rowing and looked up with blank surprise at the circling Sunderland, shielding their eyes from the sun with their hands.

Then the aircraft came in on a long, descending run, lower and lower, until she touched the surface of the Yangtse and sent up a silvery tail of flying spray. She landed on the port side of *Amethyst*, not more than seventy-five yards away.

"Row over to the aircraft!" Monaghan yelled exultantly to his oarsmen.

Then he remembered that they understood no English, and pointed urgently. The coolies rowed over to the flying-boat.

The Navy M.O. was still busily packing medical supplies when the Sunderland hit the water. Just as the aircraft slowed to a stop Fearnley heard the sharp crack of a gun, and then, following very quickly, another and another.

"The Communists have opened fire!" Jefferson exclaimed.

Fearnley looked through a port and saw a sampan approaching the aircraft with three Chinese and a naval officer on board.

"You'd better get ready to get into the sampan," Jefferson said tersely. Without pausing to think, Fearnley grabbed a haversack filled with medical supplies.

At that moment the door of the flying-boat opened, and Monaghan tumbled in. His face was flushed.

"They're very accurate," he said, shaking his head.

Through the open door Fearnley saw that the Chinese in the sampan, two men and a boy, were preparing to shove off. He jumped out into the sampan.

What happened to Fearnley in the next few moments has since struck him as having all the required ingredients of first-class slapstick. At the time no such thought occurred to him.

As soon as he landed in the sampan the Chinese, terrified at the noise of the guns, which were now popping off every few seconds, started to row madly away from the Sunderland. Their one idea was to get out of the line of fire. They rowed neither in unison nor in the same direction.

An air-burst exploded almost directly over the Sunderland, and the sampan, hysterically manned by its stampeding crew, started going round and round in tight, frantic circles. Meanwhile, to avoid certain destruction, Letford taxied the Sunderland round and started on a take-off. The Navy doctor and Monaghan and most of the medical supplies were still in the aircraft.

Fearnley was himself badly orientated. He did not know which bank of the river was north, and dangerous, and which south, and safe. All he knew was that he wanted to go to the ship, now about fifty yards away.

All the oarsmen knew was that they wanted to go ashore and start running.

"Go to the ship!" Fearnley yelled to the three Chinese.

When they made no sign of understanding him Fearnley

stood up in the shallow-draught sampan. It began to rock dangerously. The Chinese began to scream. One of them grabbed at Fearnley's trouser-legs and tried to pull him down.

Then Fearnley saw the glint of metal in the bottom of the sampan. It came from a revolver which Monaghan had dropped into the sampan when he had stepped into the aircraft. One of the Chinese, following his look, made a quick grab for it, but Fearnley's fingers closed on the weapon first. He waved it towards the ship. The sampan was still going madly round in circles. Shells were landing in the water and shooting up giant mushrooms of spray.

Softly Fearnley began to swear. He was frightened, but he was comforted by the realization that the Chinese were even more frightened. He grabbed a loose oar and tried to straighten out the sampan and head it towards the ship. He wanted to get to the ship and out of the sampan.

The Chinese shook their heads, jabbered in unmusical hysteria, pointed to the south shore, and tried, without any measure of success, to row towards it. Their oars were at odds with one another. Fearnley jabbed a finger towards the ship. "No! Not that way! This way!"

Then, as the Sunderland took off, the Communist guns followed it into the air. Fearnley, with the revolver still in his hand, persuaded the Chinese to row him to *Amethyst*. He was exhausted. It was not until considerably later that he broke the revolver open and found that it was not loaded.

Fearnley was greeted by Weston as he boarded *Amethyst*. "Good afternoon," Fearnley said. He was still a little out of breath. "I'm the doctor."

Weston nodded. "Yes. We can use you." He sounded very businesslike.

Fearnley let his eyes wander round the ship. Then he realized how serious the situation was. There were shell-holes wherever he looked. There were dead piled together. Weston, leaning on a stick, looked bloodless and ill.

Weston asked a sailor to take Fearnley down to the mess deck, where the wounded were. He didn't mention the fact that he was wounded himself.

Fearnley looked round the mess-deck with a feeling of shock. By then the Communists had switched their fire from the flying-boat to the ship. The wounded were lying close together. Fearnley saw that there was nothing he could do to save some of them. Several of the others had extensive wounds and needed hospital attention, but conditions on *Amethyst* were like those in a first-aid post. The early shelling had put the sick bay entirely out of commission.

"This is hopeless," Fearnley thought, despairingly. It was an impossible task, especially for a twenty-five-year-old who had just completed his medical training.

Meanwhile, because of the Communist fire, Weston ordered *Amethyst's* bow to be moved up into the near-by Hsiao-ho Creek. There she was partly protected from the battery on the north shore at San-chiang-ying.

Just before Fearnley's arrival on *Amethyst* Monaghan had brought a Chinese Nationalist Army doctor and his two wound-dressers to the ship. With one of the Chinese stewards acting as interpreter, the Nationalist doctor said to Fearnley, "I will go ashore and get sampans. Then I will take the wounded to hospital."

Fearnley agreed that this was the best course of action. It would be the only chance of recovery for some of the more seriously wounded. Many would probably otherwise get gas gangrene.

A couple of hours later the Chinese doctor returned, bringing with him a flotilla of eight sampans. While he was gone Fearnley had given Skinner blood plasma, and, with McCarthy as his aide, had shot morphia and penicillin into the other wounded men. He worked feverishly, trying to accomplish as much as possible in the little time he had. He hoped the penicillin would be continued when the men reached hospital.

It was not until after Fearnley had attended all the wounded on the mess-deck that Strain came down and said, "The First Lieutenant's pretty bad, Doc. So is Berger. Can you come up and see them now?"

Fearnley went up. He found Berger, Weston, and Wilkinson on the bridge.

"Look, Geoff,' Wilkinson was saying to Weston, "what about making a dash down the river for Shanghai?"

Weston shook his head regretfully. "I'm sorry, Chief; I'd like to. But our orders are to go to Nanking."

It was almost pitch-dark. Wilkinson climbed down from the bridge. He thought he saw something approaching the ship from up-river, and stood there at the rail for an instant trying to make out what it was. Then he saw that a fleet of sampans was approaching from *Amethyst's* port bow. He dragged himself round the forecastle to the wireless office to tell Hett. "There are sampans coming," he said. "I think it's an attempted Communist attack!"

"Yes, I know about them," Hett said easily. "The sampans are to evacuate the remaining wounded."

Wilkinson's leg was becoming quite stiff. He climbed with some difficulty back up to the bridge.

Fearnley had examined Berger first. He found him peppered with shell-splinters. There were bits of metal all up and down his legs, and he had several jagged wounds in his chest-wall. Fearnley shook his head, marvelling, when he was told that Berger had been active all the previous day, and had insisted on being carried to the bridge for duty that morning.

Weston, he saw now, had a wound in the right side of his chest.

"You've coughed blood?"

"Some."

"You must have a bit of shell-splinter still in your lung," Fearnley said. "You ought to go ashore to hospital with the others."

"I can't go," Weston said stiffly. "If I do there would only be one executive officer on board. That isn't enough to operate the ship."

"Come on, Geoff," Wilkinson said; "you'd better come with us. You're in no shape to stay. Listen to what the Doc. says."

Hett, Strain, and Berger joined in, all trying to persuade him to go.

"No," Weston said stubbornly. This was his first command, and he took his responsibilities very seriously. He appealed to Fearnley. "Look, Doc, won't I get better anyway, whether I go or stay?"

"I can't promise that," Fearnley said. "You must have hospital treatment. If you remain you'll be no good to the ship very soon, anyway—perhaps as early as to-morrow. And you have a good chance of dying if you stay."

Weston had a spasm of pain. "Well, I won't go."

"You must come with us, Geoff," Wilkinson said. "If you don't you may be a dead man in the morning."

"I'm perfectly capable of commanding the ship." Weston seemed to have no regard for his own safety.

Wilkinson pulled Fearnley aside. He was very anxious about Weston. He whispered to the R.A.F. doctor that he ought to give Weston a hypodermic that would put him to sleep, so that the others could take him to hospital without his knowledge.

Fearnley shook his head slowly. "Weston is in command," he said. "I can't do that."

Wilkinson threw his hands up in a gesture of surrender.

"Oh, well," he conceded, "it would have been quite a battle, anyway, even with Geoff wounded, trying to puncture him against his will. Perhaps it's all for the best."

Then Wilkinson and the other wounded (including Skinner), escorted and helped by Able Seaman Raymond Calcott and a few unwounded shipmates, boarded the last sampans. Fearnley tried one last time to persuade Weston to go to hospital, but it was of no use.

"Well," he said, finally, "I can't *make* you go."

Weston grinned. "Don't you think your last few minutes

of arguing have been slightly academic?" He pointed to the flotilla of sampans.

The last one was now several hundred yards up-river.

A signal came through from Hong Kong ordering *Amethyst* ten miles up-river before moonrise. This was to take her out of range of the Communist battery at San-chiang-ying. Moonrise was due at one o'clock in the morning.

Shortly after the sampans had gone Weston suffered an unusually great spasm of pain. He began to pant again, and was unable to talk in a way that could be understood. Fearnley gave him a stiff shot of morphia, and presently he went to sleep, still sitting up, just as the sun set behind the low hills.

He awoke at midnight. Fearnley was at his side.

"I'd better give you some benzedrine now," Fearnley told him, "to keep you awake."

Weston yawned. He felt much better after his rest. He took the benzedrine.

"I'll find out if they've got steam up," he said, getting to his feet.

Hett, Strain, Weston, and Fearnley were now the only officers on board *Amethyst*. Hett was busy in the chartroom, working out the navigation problems for the ten-mile trip up-river. Strain, Weston, and Fearnley climbed to the bridge.

It was pitch-dark. As the ship pulled her bow out of the creek they held their breath, expecting Communist gunfire at any moment. None came.

The ship moved the ten miles up the Yangtse without incident. Then she dropped anchor noisily. At once machine-guns stuttered at her from the south bank. Nervous Nationalist infantrymen, hearing the clatter of the falling anchor, had mistaken the ship for a Communist vessel attempting a river-crossing.

Weston ordered the Union Jack on the port side, facing the Communists, to be illuminated. In spite of this the firing continued. Then he ordered the anchor up, and the ship sailed a mile downstream. There was no new outbreak of firing at this anchorage.

Fearnley administered morphia to Weston once again, so that he could sleep.

"I'm getting to be a mere mechanical man," Weston grinned, "with no impulses of my own." Then Fearnley went to sleep in a camp-bed down on the mess-deck.

All was quiet again.

Chapter Sixteen

TRAIN FOR SHANGHAI

At about the same time that Fearnley was giving benzedrine to Weston—shortly after midnight—Calcott, guarding the wounded on shore, saw Kerans and made himself known.

"I'm from the Embassy in Nanking," Kerans said. "Come to one side and tell me what's up."

They moved to one side.

"I've got four wounded with me here, sir," Calcott said, "and twelve others have gone on ahead with Chinese stretcher-bearers. One of those who have gone ahead is the captain, Lieutenant-Commander Skinner."

"Is he hurt badly?"

"He's pretty bad, sir."

"Where is *Amethyst*?" Kerans asked.

"About half a mile from here."

The Chinese doctor who had been on board *Amethyst* and who had brought the sampan evacuation fleet was also accompanying the four wounded men. He was a short man, wrapped in a blanket because of the cold. He bowed and, unfolding the blanket from around him for no longer than was necessary, gave his card to Kerans with a quick little flourish. The card read: "Lieutenant Chu Wei, First-grade Surgeon."

Calcott had remained behind with the four wounded because one of them was a close friend, lingering between life and death. He wanted to remain with him until the end, and to do everything he could for him while he still had a spark of life.

Packard, the American doctor, and his assistant decided that, since the wounded had been evacuated from *Amethyst*, they should return to Tachung with Calcott's four charges; but Kerans' orders were still firm for him to board the ship.

He arranged for coolies to take him out to her in a sampan. From the shore he could just make out the frigate's silhouette cutting through the darkness. The coolies pushed their flat sampan out into the calm water of the creek, with Kerans in it.

Then he saw, to his horror, that *Amethyst* was moving. The ship had lifted anchor and was now on its way up-river, following instructions from Hong Kong. Kerans thought, "She's making a run for it to Nanking, and I've missed her."

"Damn!" he muttered violently. "Damn!"

The sampan took him back to shore. With Dewar-Durie and the Chinese doctor he hiked overland, up the steep hills which they had circled on the way out, and deposited the doctor at his own village. There the doctor gave the two British officers some hot tea, and they smoked cigarettes. Kerans tried to offer the doctor payment, on behalf of the British Government, for his services to *Amethyst's* wounded. This the Chinese steadfastly refused to accept, but finally Kerans made him agree to accept seven million Chinese dollars with which to buy cigarettes for his orderlies. As it happened, because of the rapid devaluation of the Chinese dollar at that critical stage in the downfall of the Nationalists, by the next day this sum was worth virtually nothing.

Kerans and Dewar-Durie continued on their way, after shaking hands with the Chinese doctor, and, at a quarter to four that morning, reached Tachung. There Kerans learned that Skinner and Winter had died.

The lorries he had brought down from Chingkiang earlier were still there. It was dark and very cold, and by now Kerans felt completely done in; but there was no rest in sight.

Kerans ordered the dead and wounded to be loaded separately into the lorries. The wounded groaned and complained dully of the cold. They had only two blankets among them. Kerans gave orders for the lorries to be packed with straw to make them more comfortable; then he went on ahead in the jeep to arrange for their reception in Chingkiang. He could not keep his teeth from chattering.

Before he left Tachung Packard had drawn Kerans aside.

"You'd better get these men down to Shanghai at once," Packard said. "They need the best of attention, and I wouldn't advise leaving them in Chingkiang."

Bearing this in mind, immediately on his arrival in Chingkiang Kerans asked the Chinese Naval Duty Officer to supply an extra coach for the Shanghai train, exclusively for the use of his wounded. The staff officer hemmed and hawed.

Then he said, "Sorry. It can't be done. The Ministry of Communications hasn't authorized it."

Kerans fortunately remembered the letter from Admiral Kwei. He produced it in triumph.

"That's different," the staff officer said at once. "That's all the authority I need." He eyed Kerans with new respect. He telephoned orders, and very soon the railway coach was at Kerans' disposal.

The lorry of wounded had arrived by then, but the one carrying the bodies of Skinner and Winter had not. "I wonder what could have happened to it," Kerans thought. The Chinese Naval Chief of Staff had told him in confidence that the Communists had now crossed the river to the west of Kiang Yin, near the railway, and, he had said, it was likely that they would cut it soon. The evacuation of Chinkiang had already been ordered. This meant that the train, scheduled to leave at ten in the morning, would undoubtedly be the last one for Shanghai. Kerans had persuaded the stationmaster to delay the train's departure so that the wounded could be loaded with appropriate care. Hundreds of Chinese civilian refugees with frightened faces were boarding the train.

While the wounded, stretched out on the station platform, were waiting to be loaded on to the train they were tended by Charlotte Dunlap, the matron in charge of an American missionary hospital in Chingkiang, and Packard gave them blood plasma and rendered first aid. Miss Dunlap, a kindly woman of about fifty-five, with grey hair and spectacles, was especially solicitous for the men.

The coach reserved for the *Amethyst* wounded had two private sleeping compartments, one at each end. The remainder of the car was filled with two-tiered berths. When Kerans entered the coach for a last-minute inspection, just before the wounded were carried in, he found a Chinese woman and her two young children in one of the private compartments. Later he learned that she was the wife of one of the station guards, who had smuggled her on board. With her, in addition to her children, was a mountain of bedding and other household property.

By then Kerans had gone a day and a night without sleep. He had hiked endless miles and had suffered from the cold and had bumped in the jeep over countless potholes, and he felt dirty and tired and worried over the two missing dead. He needed every bit of available space in the coach for his wounded. He lost his temper.

"Get the hell out of here!" he roared.

The woman cringed. She did not understand what he said, but there was no mistaking the tone in which he said it.

The stationmaster, hearing Kerans bellow, hurried in. He spoke to the woman in her own tongue, and she answered him indignantly, and the stationmaster spoke in an angrier tone, and finally the woman reluctantly withdrew with her brood and her chattels.

It was now nearly noon, and Kerans was aware that it was far too risky to hold the train up any longer for the two lost dead.

"Okay," he told the stationmaster. "Let her go. There's no hope now of the dead arriving on time."

The train began slowly to move. As it did one of the Chinese lorry-drivers came running up, waving his arms and yelling wildly.

"They've come! They've come!"

The stationmaster, as excited and relieved as Kerans, stopped the train, and the two bodies were carried aboard. The train pulled out with a low, doleful whistle, leaving a sulphurous scent behind it in the station.

Now that Kerans had got the wounded off to safety—they later reached Shanghai and were cared for aboard the United

States hospital ship *The Repose*—he telephoned his report in to Nanking.

"The only executive officers left aboard *Amethyst*," he told Donaldson, "are Weston, who is badly wounded, and Hett. I think I ought to try to get on board and take the ship up to Nanking." He had heard from the Nationalist Navy people in Chingkiang that *Amethyst* was anchored not far away.

"Do that," Donaldson said.

After that call Kerans tried to get a telephone connexion through to Kiang Yin to find out what was happening there. The Chingkiang operator reported that this was impossible, which served to confirm the information Kerans had had from the Chinese Chief of Staff regarding the Communist crossing. That dapper little officer, as well as all his colleagues, had been in a flat spin all the morning. The Nationalists at Chingkiang seemed palsied by fear that the Communist bombardment of their position would begin from the opposite shore at any moment. Men ran round Chinese Naval Headquarters as wildly and aimlessly as chickens fresh from the chopping-block.

The Nationalists had had a small beach-head on the north bank, but had withdrawn it during the night as soon as they saw that the Communists were seriously on the move. Wounded were streaming in. These unfortunate newcomers just sat about quietly and suffered, accepting their fate with neither resentment nor surprise. Kerans noticed one Chinese, a river pilot, who had had the back of his head blown off, and was doggedly trying to commit suicide by pushing his tongue down his throat. He did not know that this man had been brought out from *Amethyst* with the wounded members of the ship's crew.

Quite by accident Kerans again ran into the same young Chinese sub-lieutenant he had met on his arrival from Nanking, the one who had been aboard *Amethyst*. This time, bolstering his arguments with Admiral Kwei's letter, he was able to convince the young officer that he should take him to *Amethyst* in a landing-craft. Dewar-Durie came down to the wharf to see Kerans off, and the slim, handsome young Lieutenant-Commander, carrying charts and medical supplies, grinned a tired farewell.

It was a few minutes before two in the afternoon.

French had been on constant duty, without sleep and without leaving the wireless key, for fifty-six hours. He no longer knew what day it was or how long he had been non-stop on the job. Time passed in a foggy daze. It was remarkable that he could still maintain a high degree of accuracy in his sending and receiving. When Fearnley arrived he had been given benzedrine by the doctor, so that he would not fall asleep over his key.

Even his meals were brought to him, and he was reminded of the time of day by what he was given to eat: boiled eggs meant morning; sausages and chips, noon; rabbit pie, early evening. At times he felt groggy and light-headed, in spite of the benzedrine, but there was no one to take his place, and the job had to be done.

He stuck stubbornly to his key. For two full days and two full nights he had kept the *Amethyst's* only channel of communication open to the outside world. To all but the men on the ship he was an anonymous man tapping a steady, staccato key. Then a signal came from Vice-Admiral Madden:

SPLENDID PERFORMANCE BY ALL ON BOARD. THE WORK OF YOUR SOLE TELEGRAPHIST EVOKES MY ADMIRATION.

French was getting very sleepy again when a seaman burst into the wireless office.

"There's another Sunderland overhead! She's signalling with lights, but there's no one to read them."

"Hang on," French signalled to Hong Kong.

He dashed up to the bridge to read the light signals from the circling Sunderland, but his unbroken hours at the key without rest had sapped his faculties. He saw more lights than there were: first two, and then apparently more than two, and then two again. They were all blinking dizzily.

"How many lights are there?" he asked.

"Why, one," Hett said, surprised. "Only one."

"I'm sorry," French admitted. "I can't seem to read it."

"Just signal that it's safe to land," some one told him. French did so. The Sunderland came down. Just as it touched the Yangtse the Communist guns opened fire on it, and the flying-boat revved up its motors with a snarling roar and took off. It faded into the distant sky.

When Griffiths heard the Sunderland coming in for its landing he was having a shower-bath. Since he had been cleaning dried blood from his hair he was crowned with a white, foaming lather of soap. When he heard the first Communist shots some deep, warning instinct told him to get out of the bathroom as quickly as he could. Naked, he stepped at once out into the passage.

Just as the door slammed shut behind him a shell crashed through what sounded like a near-by bulkhead. He opened the door and looked back into the room he had just left. It was blurred with bitter-smelling smoke. A gaping hole let daylight through the bulkhead. Twisted water-pipes flooded the floor.

"The shell," he told his mates a few minutes later, still shaking and pale, "burst in the showers—right where I'd been standing!"

Amethyst, Kerans had learned at Chingkiang, was now four and a half miles below that city. The landing-craft, one of many American war-surplus craft in the Far East, moved along, hugging the south bank, and, where the river narrowed suddenly, took cover behind a small island called Chiao Shan. The island rose, pyramid-like, out of the water, and was crowned by a shining temple, complete with pagoda. Along the south bank the grass was very green. Plank jetties stuck out into the water like serrated teeth. Kerans heard the buzz of an aircraft, and, looking up, saw a Sunderland circling down-river.

It took about an hour to get from Chingkiang to the ship.

As he approached, but was still several hundred yards from the ship, *Amethyst* did not appear to Kerans to be seriously damaged. No one was moving on her upper deck, yet he had the strange feeling that he was being watched.

Below-decks McNamara and Rees heard the look-out yell, "Craft approaching downstream!"

The two made their way carefully to a sheltered part of the upper deck. They saw Strain and Hett come quietly out of the wireless office, taking cover, to look at the craft through glasses.

"Think it's a Communist attack?" McNamara asked thinly.

"Damned if I know," Rees said. "Perhaps we'd better set up a Bren gun and cover the landing-craft with it."

"Sure thing, Fatso. Good idea."

The two set the gun up on its tripod and waited, ready to shoot. Other men had, unknown to them, already been detailed to cover the approaching craft.

Strain caught sight of them crouched behind the gun. "Hey," he said anxiously, "don't fire without provocation."

Then McNamara jumped to his feet. "Look, Fatso!" His voice was filled with excitement. "There's a naval officer on board! Maybe he's that Lieutenant-Commander from Nanking." A signal had reached the ship earlier that day advising *Amethyst* to expect Kerans' arrival, and word had filtered down to the crew and had caused an excited buzz of speculation.

"Perhaps it is," Rees said. "It's good to see some one from outside."

"Yeah. Do you suppose now we're going to make a run for it?"

Strain's voice came to them then, high and tense. "Put the Bren out of the way," Strain said. "Put it out of the way."

As Kerans approached *Amethyst* in the landing-craft he saw

that his first impression that there was not much damage to the ship had been premature and inaccurate. There were jagged shell-holes everywhere. The deck was covered with debris, but there was still no movement visible in the ship. For a moment he feared that it had been abandoned.

Then, as the landing-craft came alongside, Jack Walker, a stocky, ruddy-faced able seaman, bobbed up. "Glad to see you, sir!" Walker said, sounding as if he meant it.

Hett came over to the side of the ship. He reached down to grip Kerans' hand and help him aboard.

"What was that Sunderland doing?" Kerans asked.

"It was trying to land a padre to bury the dead," Hett said. "It was fired at, though, and couldn't get him off."

Kerans nodded. "Where's Weston?"

Hett led the way to the wireless office. Weston greeted him from where he sat, stiffly, in his canvas-bottomed chair. He grinned up at Kerans.

"Have a horse's neck?" Weston offered. There was still nothing else he could keep down. He was beginning to show the effects of his long fight against pain. There was a tautness to his face that had not been there the day before. He and Kerans shook hands. Then Kerans turned to Fearnley.

"Is this officer fit to carry on?"

Fearnley shook his head. "No. He ought to go ashore to hospital. He should have gone earlier with the others."

Weston cleared his throat angrily. "I don't want to go. I feel all right. *I'm not going.*"

"I'm sorry," Kerans said, "but I'm afraid I'll have to order you to go."

Weston tried to hide his bitter disappointment. He tried very hard to think up an acceptable excuse, so that he could remain on board.

"There wouldn't be time for me to get my gear together," he offered feebly. "The landing-craft can't wait that long."

"You have your orders," Kerans said.

Weston sighed. He tried to grin, but he couldn't quite bring it off. "Well, cheerio, then," he said. "I hope we all meet in the Gripps." The Gripps was the Navy name for the bar on the top floor of the Hong Kong Hotel.

A moment later the landing-craft chugged away in the direction of Chingkiang with Weston on board. French handed Kerans a message which indicated that the Yangtse had indeed been crossed near Nanking by the Communists, and which instructed him not to move *Amethyst*.

The ship was now in an exceedingly unfortunate position, and there seemed, for the time at least, to be nothing that could be done to relieve it.

She was trapped in the Yangtse between two major Communist assault crossings—at Kiang Yin and near Nanking—and it was becoming increasingly obvious that any fresh movement of the ship, either up- or down-river, would result in further serious loss of life, and quite possibly in the destruction of *Amethyst* herself.

About eighty officers and men, both wounded and able-bodied, had been evacuated from the ship at different times; eighty-one, including Kerans and eight Chinese, now remained. Kerans had noted that nearly all the life-saving apparatus—Carley floats and lifeboats—had been destroyed in the shelling, or had been lost in the confused and piecemeal evacuation. Only one damaged whaler remained, and it was not sound enough to rely upon.

At eight o'clock that evening Kerans received a signalled order from Vice-Admiral Madden, acting Commander-in-Chief, Far East Station:

THE SAFETY OF YOUR SHIP'S COMPANY BEING NOW THE FIRST CONSIDERATION YOU ARE NOW TO PREPARE TO EVACUATE FROM THE SHIP AND SINK. REPORT WHEN YOU WILL BE READY. ACKNOWLEDGE.

Chapter Seventeen

PINNED DOWN

His first job after he took over command of *Amethyst*, Kerans decided, was to bury the dead. They had been awaiting burial now for more than fifty hours, because of the anticipated arrival of the chaplain by Sunderland, and the weather by day had begun to turn hot. It was obvious that there should not be any further delay. He had Petty Officer Jeremiah Murphy brought to the wireless office.

"As I understand it," Kerans said, "you are the senior Roman Catholic rating on board. Is that correct?"

"Yes, sir, I am."

"Right. Then you will bury the Roman Catholics. I will be responsible for the others."

The bodies were sewn into hammocks, and each one was weighted with two four-inch shells. It was a simple burial service. Kerans could not fire the customary three rifle-volleys for fear the Communists, believing that they were being fired upon, would retaliate.

They piped the dead over the side. Each one, weighted with the live shells, fell with a splash and sank quickly down into the mud of the river-bed. The whole ceremony took about twenty minutes.

Then Kerans divided the ship's company into groups, and gave each group a task towards preparing the ship for sinking. Because of the nearness of the Nationalist forces he decided that it would not be wise to set fire to the ship, as this might draw the attention of the Communist guns and cause casualties on the south shore. He could not, in addition, sink the ship in deep water, since so much of the life-saving equipment had been destroyed. He settled finally on a plan to beach the ship, open all the sea-cocks, and set off an explosion to destroy her. He himself would remain behind to set off the explosion after all the others had reached shore in safety.

By ten that night arrangements for the destruction of the remaining classified material had been completed, and other preparations for abandoning and blowing up the ship had been made. Kerans did not know that at this very time high-level discussions were going on in Nanking and Hong Kong regarding the proposed sinking of *Amethyst*. The final decision to sink or not to sink had not been made.

Meanwhile Kerans planned that after the order came and was carried out he would lead his men on foot along the banks of the Grand Canal to Shanghai. It would be a two-hundred-and-fifty-mile march, and Kerans was far from certain that it could be done.

At midnight French received a message for Kerans. It said that the order to evacuate and sink *Amethyst* would not be given that night.

The men slept.

By dawn of April the 23rd *Amethyst* was washed by a thick, rolling fog. From the deck neither bank of the river could be seen. Then, at about nine in the morning, the sun burned through, revealing an eerily lifeless river, quiet and unaccustomedly empty.

There was nothing but *Amethyst* afloat. There were no signs of Nationalist troops on the south bank, as there had been the day before. It was an unnatural stillness, and the men, feeling this, kept glancing at the north shore. There should have been life on the banks of the river, and there should have been Chinese fishermen after the tiny, bony fish of the Yangtse, and there should have been junks sailing by. There was only silence and empty space.

Shortly after midday Kerans saw the first movement of Communist troops on the north shore. This made him believe a battery site was being established to cover a crossing which would lead into the Grand Canal. The canal had an outlet on the south bank near where *Amethyst* was anchored, and the

Communists would doubtless make use of the waterway to transport their supplies as they fought on towards Shanghai.

This, Kerans decided, would make *Amethyst's* position not only uncomfortable and dangerous, but untenable. It meant that the ship would be in the direct flow of Communist assault craft when they came. There was no telling what might happen in such circumstances.

He decided to shift *Amethyst's* berth downstream and to anchor opposite a stretch of shore which held no cover in which to establish a battery of heavy guns. He weighed anchor and sailed down-stream, and just as he was about to drop anchor again the ship came under artillery-fire. The shells came from Yu-lung-chow, a small island, or perhaps from a point of land just behind it.

Amethyst whipped round at full speed. She reanchored close to the south bank, between the two villages of Ma-chia-shaw and Chen-pi Chen-kou. The firing stopped after several near misses that struck water about ten yards from the ship. There had been no hits.

By then Kerans realized that the Communist guns were sited to cover every foot of the vital reaches of the river. There was no escaping their ever-present threat.

The situation was once again a desperate one. Kerans, with his damaged ship and depleted ship's company, could man and fight only one four-inch gun in local control and a single Oerlikon. There seemed no hope of movement either up river or down without heavy loss of life.

"The Communists," he thought grimly, just as Weston had done before him, "can destroy us whenever they choose."

Chapter Eighteen

SLEEP AT LAST

Another signal came through from Vice-Admiral Madden:

FRENCH SHOULD GET SOME SLEEP. ARRANGE WHEN WE SHOULD CALL YOU AGAIN.

French closed down his connexion with Hong Kong. He fell asleep that night in the wireless office with his chair tilted back against the bulkhead and wearing his earphones. He had turned the volume up, so that if any urgent message came through the sound of it would awaken him. He slept for three hours, and then, cramped by his uncomfortable position, awoke. He was still very tired.

Meanwhile Kerans sent word round the ship that if there were any men on board who had ever learned Morse they should report at once to him. Two men, Rutter and Blomley, came forward. Neither was qualified to send or to receive, but each, years before, had learned the Morse alphabet. They admitted that they had forgotten much of it. Kerans took them in to see French, who was on duty again.

"The call-sign," French explained, "is SQT. I'll ask Hong Kong to send it very long and very slow, and when you hear it coming over you can shake me awake, and I'll take over."

Then, while French caught up on his lost sleep, the two men took turns with the earphones.

Chapter Nineteen

WITH THE COMMUNISTS

Bannister and Martin, at the Stevenson Mission Hospital in Changchow, fearfully awaited their first contact with the Communist captors of the city. During the afternoon of the day the city was taken Bannister watched bands of green-uniformed Communist soldiers wandering round the hospital grounds gawking and sightseeing. Groups of a score or more paraded through the hospital corridors and came into the room that the two British sailors shared, eyeing them silently and going out again. They looked very grim and serious.

That evening a Communist General came to visit the two sailors. He could not have been more than five feet tall. He wore a pair of pearl-handled revolvers in hip-holsters and a bright red bandana stuck carelessly in his wide leather belt.

He introduced himself. "You are from the ship *Amethyst*?"

To make sure that the two sailors understood he wrote the name of the ship, in English, on a piece of paper and showed it to them.

"Yes," Bannister said.

"What do you want me to do?"

Banister and Martin exchanged a quick look. Bannister said, "I want you to take us back to the ship."

The little General shook his head. "No can do now," he said. His English was perfectly understandable, but somewhat makeshift. "My armies advancing to Shanghai."

Bannister sighed. He hadn't really expected anything more. "Well, have you seen *Amethyst*?" Neither he nor Martin had had any way of learning if the ship still existed, or if it had been blown out of the water by the Communists. They waited, scarcely breathing, for the General's reply. Bannister was being conscientiously careful of every word he said. He didn't want to reveal any information which might be of value to the General, but he wanted desperately to hear news of the ship.

The General thought about it for a moment, as if he too were weighing each word.

"Yes, I have seen your ship."

"Are there any people on board?"

The General seemed to have some difficulty with Bannister's Irish brogue. Bannister repeated the question.

"Yes," the General said tersely. He had been seated on a chair between the two single beds. Now he rose to his feet. "Good-bye," he said, and departed as abruptly as he had arrived.

For their first two meals in hospital the two sailors were given rice dishes. Then Martin, Leicester-born and sceptical of all cooking that was not English, broached the subject to Mary Wong.

"I've been wondering," he said, "if you have any English food here at the hospital."

Mrs Wong's gentle face took on an air of concern. "I'm sorry, no; we haven't any English food," she said. "We do have some tins the Americans left behind when they went. Would that do?"

Martin said that it would do very well. For the remainder of their stay at the hospital Bannister and he varied their rice diet with the American tinned food.

Four days after the General's visit Mrs Wong came to see them again.

"Two Communist soldiers are in my office," she said. "They wish to speak to you."

Bannister and Martin were feeling much better. They put on white hospital dressing-gowns and slippers and walked down to Mrs Wong's office. The two Communists were there, waiting solemnly. The four sat silently examining one another, while Mrs Wong fetched pale tea in tall glasses. Then she said, "These two soldiers bring you good news. They say you are going to be taken back to your ship in a few days." She smiled. "You must hurry to get well."

They left the hospital on a Sunday, ten days later. Before they left Mrs Wong, who had become quite attached to the two young men, said, "Would you like to come to church before you go?"

To please her Bannister said, "Yes, we'd like that."

The service was in Chinese. Neither sailor understood a word.

At seven in the evening they dressed in brown hospital shirts and white American Navy pyjama trousers, and white flannel hospital dressing-gowns. Mrs Wong showed them to the door of the hospital, where the hospital chaplain, the superintendent, and several nurses shook hands and wished them luck. Mrs Wong, dressed in her plain pale-blue gown. had tears gathering in her eyes as she said good-bye.

Bannister and Martin didn't know what to say. They were most grateful for the kindnesses and care they had received, but when it came to saying so they found themselves inarticulate.

"Thank you," Bannister said simply, "for everything you did for us."

"Me too," Martin said.

They both coloured with embarrassment, aware that they should have said more, but not knowing how to say it.

Two rickshaws were waiting for them. They climbed in, and the coolies padded through the narrow, cobbled streets that soon widened into the more modern thoroughfares in the centre of the city. Green-suited Communists were everywhere.

The rickshaws stopped at a large brick building, which was the Chinese People's Liberation Army headquarters for that sector. Bannister and Martin climbed out and waited at the entrance of the building, feeling lost and not knowing what to do.

Presently a soldier came out of the building, carrying a sheaf of papers. He looked them up and down, and then nodded and motioned for them to follow after him. He led the way to an Army lorry, guarded by three armed and uniformed Communists.

He signalled for them to climb on to the back platform of the lorry. The three guards climbed quietly up with them, and the lorry drove off.

Then Bannister began to be teased by doubts. "Are they really taking us to the ship?" he worried.

They drove on through the night. At one in the morning they came to another town, and the lorry stopped in front of a large house. They were in Chingkiang, but Bannister and Martin did not know it. Communist soldiers poured out of the house. One of them, a huge man with a very wide, flat face, held a candle close to their faces. In English he said, "Why did you fight with us?" He seemed quite belligerent.

"We didn't want to," Bannister said defensively, "but you fired first. We had to save ourselves."

The big man grunted sceptically. "Come inside with me." He had large, even teeth which gleamed in the candle-light. He took them inside, and gave them warm water to drink and peanuts to eat.

They were now in a large, well-lit living-room. An officer, sitting in a comfortably padded armchair, leaned forward and offered them a packet of cigarettes.

"Thank you," Bannister said, accepting the packet. The officer waved his arm, as if dismissing his generosity.

"You British," a frankly admiring voice said behind them, "are very tough." They turned. It was the big soldier with the gleaming teeth. He sat down beside them and told them about his family, which, he said sadly, was very far away. Then he interpreted for the officer, who spoke wistfully of his own wife and two children.

With surprised relief, Bannister thought, "Anyway, they don't seem to mean us any harm."

After a while the big soldier said, "I'm sure you must be tired and would like to sleep."

"Yes," Bannister agreed, "we would."

The big one showed the way across a garden into another

Some of "Amethyst's" Crew

Another Photograph of Some of the Crew

Heath (back row) and Bannister are circled. These photographs were taken to help to relieve boredom.

More of the Crew
McNamara, Garns, and McCarthy are circled

Kerans' "Glamour Boys"

house. They climbed up steep stairs to a small attic with one window. They slept that night on beds made of doors placed across boxes, with bureau drawers for pillows, and with a little straw spread over the doors and bureau drawers to make the improvised beds slightly less uncomfortable. The beds were very hard, but Bannister and Martin were too exhausted to notice. There was a single candle in the room, which they didn't bother to snuff out. Just before they fell asleep they heard a guard snoring outside the attic door.

Next morning they were awakened by the sound of some one humming, and as they opened their eyes two soldiers came through the door carrying wash-basins and water. For breakfast they had two hard-boiled eggs and a bowl of rice each. With the bowls of rice were chopsticks. They had never tried to use them before.

They peeled the shells off the eggs and ate them in their hands, all the time looking at the chopsticks and wondering about them. Then they tried picking the rice up with them.

"I can't seem to get the hang of this," Martin said. "I keep dropping most of the rice."

Bannister shook his head. "It beats me."

The guards saw their trouble, and made eager signs, indicating that they should hold the bowls very near their open mouths and use the two sticks together to scoop up the rice. They tried it that way, and found the method very satisfactory.

The sun, beating down hard on the attic roof, made the room very hot. After a while Bannister became bored at his inactivity and rolled some newspapers into a ball and tossed the ball to Martin. The two patted the paper ball back and forth for a while, and their two grinning guards soon signified that they would like to join in the fun. The idea was to keep the ball from touching the floor. The four of them, prisoners and guards, played at the game for more than an hour.

At about noon Bannister and Martin were taken back to the big house they had entered on their arrival the night before. They were given a room containing one single bed for the two of them, and were told that they could have the freedom of the

H

house. They could walk through any of the rooms, but they were not to go outside.

Bannister strolled round the house. Half a dozen soldiers were cleaning rifles and revolvers industriously. One motioned Bannister over. He was cleaning two automatic revolvers. He pointed to the nameplate on one of them, where it said "Made in U.S.A."

He shook his head. Then, very seriously, he said to Bannister, "No good. No good."

Bannister pretended not to understand.

A captain who spoke a little English, a very small man with a round, guileless face, signalled Bannister into another room.

He indicated a large wall map of the world, and pointed first to China and then to Britain.

"Far away," he said. Over the map was a photograph of Mao Tse-tung, the Chinese Communist leader.

"Yes," Bannister said, thinking of Belfast, "far away."

Chapter Twenty

SAMPAN

Even though, during the afternoon of the 23rd of April, after the abnormal calm, strong assault crossings of the Yangtse were made both ahead and astern of the ship by the Communists, the order to sink and abandon *Amethyst* was never given. The high officers in Nanking and Hong Kong had changed their minds.

The ship was not molested during the crossings, and Kerans could not help feeling that this was because the Communist leaders felt that the opposing Nationalist Army was their primary adversary, and that any attention they might care to pay the British frigate would keep safely until later.

Kerans watched the Communist crossings with an uneasy but fascinated interest. Junks, small boats—some of them propelled by outboard motors—and sailing craft by steady hundreds passed the trapped British ship, each one loaded deep with troops and stores. They reached the south bank without Nationalist opposition of any kind.

While this steady, unnerving flow of Communist troops and supplies passed *Amethyst* Kerans kept his men busy. He thought it would be bad for their morale if they had the idle time in which to think of what *might* happen if the Communists chose to turn their attention from the Nationalists to *Amethyst*. He ordered the ship to be cleared of litter and debris, and it was done.

"Sandbag the wireless office," he said then. "Sandbag the bridge, the wheelhouse, the charthouse, and the habitable mess-decks. Make *Amethyst* as splinter-proof as possible. If we haven't enough sand use the bags of flour the ship was taking to the Embassy in Nanking. If we haven't enough bags use mattresses, cushion-covers, canvas kitbags. Anything."

This also was done.

At five o'clock on the morning of Sunday, the 24th of April, *Amethyst* listed suddenly and without warning to port. Kerans' heart sank; but he quickly ordered an inspection.

This revealed that the list had been caused by water which had poured through a hole on the waterline and which had seeped through weakened plates.

"Jettison top-weight and pump out the hold," was the remedy Kerans prescribed. To the relief of all on board, this brought *Amethyst* back on an even keel. The next few days passed without excitement. Soon civilian junk traffic reappeared on the Yangtse. But the tension on board the ship did not lift.

Both banks of the river were now firmly in Communist hands. *Amethyst* was ringed in even more tightly and dangerously than before. If they chose, the Communists could now rip her apart with a withering crossfire.

On the 26th of April the ship had her first direct contact with the Communists. Just after one o'clock in the afternoon three green-clad soldiers, accompanied by two civilians, appeared on the south bank near the ship. They waved their arms and shouted to attract *Amethyst's* attention.

"Send But Sai Tin up to the bridge to interpret," Kerans ordered. But Sai Tin was Kerans' Chinese steward. He arrived on the bridge, but a high, whistling wind, raising white caps on the surface of the river, made the shouts from shore unintelligible.

Two hours later, when the wind had died to a plaintive whisper, the Communists returned. They resumed their waving and shouting. Kerans sent for But Sai Tin once again.

The steward cocked his head to one side and listened carefully.

"They say come ashore and talk," he told Kerans.

"I'll send a deputy," Kerans said.

But Sai Tin shouted the message ashore, and Kerans,

following it up, called for volunteers to row in to the south bank in the leaking whaler, and for a petty officer to lead them. Petty Officer Freeman stepped forward at once with a kind of rushed eagerness to be first, as did more men than were needed. A trip ashore is, to a sailor, a welcome change in virtually any circumstances.

Kerans looked them over. "Boys and non-swimmers," he ordered crisply, "fall out!" When this was done there were still plenty of men to handle the whaler.

Kerans' spell as Assistant Naval Attaché to the Embassy in Nanking had taught him a few things about the Chinese character. He knew how much stress these people put on what they call 'face'—a self-esteem which is expected to be shared and recognized by others. With this in mind he had Freeman dress in Lieutenant Strain's uniform. Food and cigarettes were packed in the whaler, just in case the unexpected happened and the men were unable to get back to the ship.

As soon as the boat touched shore Freeman, with But Sai Tin as his interpreter, was escorted to a near-by peasant's cottage, where he was introduced to Major Kung, a precise little Chinese officer with searching black eyes.

Meanwhile a group of peasants dressed in baggy trousers and loose blouses crowded round the beached whaler, staring at the men from *Amethyst* with big, curious eyes and whispering among themselves in hushed tones, as if the sailors had come, not from a British warship, but from the moon.

In the cottage Kung grinned knowingly at Freeman. "I," he said, "am the battery commander from San-chiang-ying." It was from this battery that the shells had come which had hit *Amethyst* and had driven her aground on Rose Island. Kung paused for a moment to observe the effect of this statement on Freeman. When he saw that Freeman retained his calm Kung added, "I wish to make it clear that *Amethyst* will not be molested provided she does not move, and also provided there is no trouble from the ship. Of course, you realize that this never would have happened if you had not fired first." He paused again, and this time he drew blood.

"*You* fired first," Freeman said icily, "and you know it. Furthermore, our captain demands a safe-passage down the river."

"I can't grant you a safe-passage," Kung said. "It is not for me to decide. It is up to the authorities in Nanking." By then the Chinese People's Liberation Army had set up a headquarters there. Kung pursed his lips and looked up at Freeman, narrowing his dark eyes. "I wonder if you realize that British gunfire caused more than two hundred and fifty casualties to Communist soldiers and local peasants in the neighbourhood of San-chiang-ying?"

"I wouldn't know about that," Freeman said; but he was surprised to hear that *Consort*, *Amethyst*, and, perhaps, *London* had inflicted such heavy casualties. "There must have been a terrific concentration of troops in the area, waiting to cross the river," he thought. He told the Major of *Amethyst's* lack of boats. Even the whaler, he pointed out, was in very sad shape and might not last.

"I'll send a sampan and its crew out for your use," Kung promised. "Then you can contact us whenever you wish." He bowed with deep formality.

The first interview was ended.

On the next day, April the 27th, Kerans was asked by the Communists to go ashore to have a further meeting with Kung. He turned the invitation down on the grounds that he did not intend to leave the ship until the situation became more static. He sent Hett ashore as his deputy. Little was accomplished.

On the 28th the sampan arrived.

It was operated by three women, two of them in their early twenties, the third wrinkled and aged. One of the younger women carried a baby.

These three Chinese females, in their small sampan, became *Amethyst's* sole contact with shore. Each morning, weather permitting—and the women seemed to have an unerring instinct for diagnosing rain or high winds—they paddled out to the ship and fastened, leechlike, to her side. Each evening they paddled ashore again. At first the rice diet of these three women was supplemented by left-overs from *Amethyst's* galley.

They were the only women *Amethyst's* men were to see for a very long time. The youngest of them, a small, very dark, and quite pretty woman, the men called Midnight. They named the ancient one Gran and the mother of the small child Cheesi.

"How about a date, Midnight?" Garns yelled, grinning, over the side. "How about a date?"

Midnight yelled back in high-pitched Chinese.

Garns asked a Chinese steward to tell him what Midnight had said in reply. The steward hesitated for a moment.

"Maybe better you not know," he said.

In all Hett had three meetings ashore with the battery commander; then Kerans took over, discussing *Amethyst's* position with the local garrison commander, a Captain Tai-ko Liang. These meetings, which always seemed to end with the British requests being diverted up a blind alley, culminated on the 18th of May in formal demands being made on *Amethyst* as a basis for further negotiations.

These came in the form of a stiff memorandum from the Communists. It stated in a preamble that the Chinese People's Liberation Army from its headquarters at Chinkiang had decided to solve, through negotiations, "all problems arising from the atrocious action of British warships in their invasion of the Chinese People's Liberation Army front and their incumbent responsibilities."

It went on to state that "Colonel Kang Mao-chao, the Political Commissar of the Third Artillery Regiment, Chingkiang Front, is the authoritative representative on the Communist side for conducting negotiations with *Amethyst*." It asked for a representative to be appointed on behalf of the Royal Navy.

Until this preliminary step was taken, the note said, there was no hope of a safe-conduct out of the river for *Amethyst*.

Kerans was dismayed thus to learn that *Amethyst's* case, instead of being placed on its proper diplomatic level, had now become a local issue.

All through the long succession of meetings which followed between Kerans and the Communists the latter repeated their three demands as prerequisites to a final discussion regarding a safe-conduct for *Amethyst*. The demands were:

First, an admission from Kerans of guilt of invasion and infringement of Chinese sovereignty by *Amethyst*.

Second, the acceptance by *Amethyst* of the onus of blame for the incident.

Third, the admission that compensation for damage and loss of life was due to the Communists.

These were demands which, of course, Kerans found it impossible to meet. Still, he kept hoping against hope for a safe-conduct.

Chapter Twenty-one

THREAT

On their third night in Chingkiang Bannister and Martin were transferred to still another house. They were being well fed and well supplied with cigarettes. In addition to the staples of rice and eggs, they had been given cabbage, lettuce, and small green onions to vary their diet. At dinner that night one of the Communist privates diffidently brought some brown sugar on a piece of paper and asked them by signs if they would like to try some on their rice. Martin, who had a sweet tooth, indicated that he would. Bannister signified that he would prefer more vegetables instead. Both wishes were granted.

The two were able to look out of a window over a parade ground where Chinese People's Liberation Army troops seemed to drill all day and all night. The soldiers sang and stamped their feet in unison. The pleasure they got out of their reedy music showed on their flat, sickly saffron faces. They liked to sing. Sometimes they would join in the chorus of a solemn song about Communism, but not always.

After they had been in the third house for a day and a night Bannister and Martin were examined by an Army doctor called Wong Wei.

"You'll be all right," he told Bannister, "so long as you don't get hit on the chest." Martin's thigh was mending nicely.

The doctor chatted with them for a while, getting more and more friendly. Finally he slung an arm affectionately round Bannister's shoulders.

"Will you sing me a song?" he asked.

By now Bannister had become accustomed to the idea that the Chinese were extremely fond of singing, but he was still surprised at their occasional displays of uninhibited sentimentality.

"What do you want me to sing?"

"That one Bing Crosby always sings."

"Which one do you mean?"

"Why, *Moonlight and Roses*."

"I didn't know he sang that number," Bannister said. "Anyway, I'm sorry, but I don't know the words."

The doctor cleared his throat happily.

"All right. Then I'll sing it to you." He proceeded to do so.

He had, Bannister decided, quite a pleasant voice; but he was no Crosby.

Then the doctor said, "My Colonel would like you both to fill in these papers to tell us what happened to you." Bannister and Martin wrote guarded reports. The doctor smiled. "If there is anything you want," he offered, "just ask for it: chicken to eat, a new suit to wear, shoes—anything."

Bannister looked down at the pyjama trousers and brown hospital shirt which he was still wearing. He thought, "If these blokes are giving stuff away we might as well ask for it."

"I could use a new suit," he said, "and underclothes. And a towel, tooth-brush, and soap."

"Me too," Martin said.

The doctor shook hands with each of them gravely and left.

Next day, somewhat to their surprise, the things they had asked for were delivered; but that night they had a less pleasant experience. At about 10 P.M. a guard came to their room.

"My Colonel would like to see you," he said. He escorted them across the street to an imposing stone house and into a large room containing a round table, four straight chairs, and no other furniture. The Colonel sat at the table.

Colonel Kang was a big man for a Chinese. His face seemed permanently cast in a grim, unhappy mould, as if he constantly had a bad taste in his mouth. A Major Yan sat beside him. The Major was small. He wore glasses. He seemed quick and intelligent.

"Your names, please?" the Major asked briskly. "Your rank? Your ship?" Then, after Bannister and Martin had replied, "The Colonel has something to say to you."

Colonel Kang looked steadily and silently at them for a long moment. Then he began to speak in loud and angry Chinese. He harangued them for ten full minutes without interruption, eyeing Bannister and Martin almost balefully and gesticulating angrily as he spoke.

"I will explain," the Major said, "what my Colonel has said to you. He is very angry with you both. Your ship entered Chinese waters and killed two hundred and fifty of his soldiers. Therefore, since you are both members of the crew of H.M.S. *Amethyst*, you cannot be left unresponsible. When we get your captain he shall die." The Major's statement of casualties inflicted by *Amethyst* was, of course, distorted, since, as Kung had previously informed Freeman, the two hundred and fifty had been both soldiers and civilians, and the shooting had been done not only by *Amethyst*, but also by the other British warships.

Bannister stood up. His naturally pink face was flushed to a deeper shade of colour.

"You opened fire on us first! It wasn't our fault!"

The Major held his hand up sternly. "Quiet! Martin may speak."

Martin said, "Well, it's true. You did open fire on us first."

The Major got stiffly to his feet. "Go back to your room. We have nothing more to say to you."

They returned to their room, talking over the meeting with Colonel Kang in worried tones. They were unable to sleep. They tossed in the narrow bed.

"Do you think they're going to shoot us?" Martin asked.

The same thought had occurred to Bannister, but he felt that, since he was the elder, he should not unduly frighten the boy-seaman.

"No," he said. "They just lost their tempers." He kept thinking over and over and over again of the menacing phrase, "you cannot be left unresponsible."

When the first shaft of daylight squeezed through their small window they were both still awake.

Chapter Twenty-two

WELCOME BACK

Next morning at ten the Major came to their room.

"I'm sorry for the way I spoke last night," he said. "You understand I have to obey orders. My Colonel was very angry, and he had every right to be. Of course, I know it isn't your fault. It's people like your captain and Churchill who are really responsible for the death of your sailors and our soldiers."

At that time the two sailors did not know that Skinner had died, and that Kerans had arrived and was in command of the ship.

Bannister and Martin were thoroughly suspicious of the Major's overtures. He talked to them all that day, remaining with them, trying to convince them that Communism was the cure for the world's ills.

He was pleasant-mannered, and well-educated, and he expressed his arguments forcibly. By the time the sun was setting, however, he saw that he was getting nowhere with the two young Britons.

He said, "Have you a sweetheart at home, Bannister?"

"Yes."

"I have a sweetheart too. I haven't been able to see her for more than a year."

Bannister was tired of listening to him, and he was particularly tired of Chinese sentimentality. "When are we going to be taken back to the ship?" he demanded.

"I can't answer that."

"Is the ship far from here?"

"Not far. I'll ask about getting you back to the ship as soon as possible," he said. Then he left.

During their long stay with the Communists Bannister tried to pick up a little Chinese. He tried to talk with the guards, and he did succeed in learning a few words—*tovar* for 'hair,' *swee* for 'lips,' *ya* for 'teeth,' *yen* for 'eyes.'

He discovered that one of the guards, a short, stocky man with flashing black eyes, had a certain earthy sense of humour. During one of his attempts to enhance his vocabulary Bannister had a session with the guard, who pointed to Bannister's face.

"*Digma*," he said.

The other guard burst into high-pitched laughter.

"*Digma*," he repeated, "*Digma, digma*." Then, translating by gesture, he patted his buttocks and burst into laughter again. Bannister, rather sheepishly, joined them with a quiet chuckle.

Another of the soldiers was very big and strong. It soon became clear that he considered himself to be irresistibly virile. He was not above behaving like a bully. One afternoon he indicated to Bannister that he would like to play a game which would involve hooking his middle fingers with Bannister's.

They hooked fingers.

Then, laughing uproarously at Bannister for falling into his trap, the Chinese pulled the sailor round the room, throwing him here and there with sudden jerks, but hanging tightly on to his fingers. He did not let go until, presently, he tired of the game.

Bannister, lips tight and eyes blazing, danced round the thick-set bully. He flicked a fist into his flat face. He did it again.

The bully's head snapped back and back again. The Chinese had never experienced this game before, and he did not like it. He retreated clumsily, but Bannister kept following after him with stinging fists, until, eventually, the bully turned and fled out of the house, shame-faced. After that he did not again offer to pull Bannister's fingers. He had lost face in the eyes of his comrades.

That night the Major called round to see them.

"I think you will be able to return to your ship in a couple of days," he said, grinning.

Bannister and Martin had almost given up hope, but now their old optimism bubbled up again. When the Communist doctor had promised them clothes they had got them. Now they had been told they would be taken back to the ship. Why shouldn't that come true as well?

The next day was May the 25th. Bannister and Martin had been away from *Amethyst* for thirty-five days. By now skilled in the use of chopsticks, they were eating their noon meal of rice and eggs when a small lorry pulled up in front of the house.

The Major bounced in, beaming. He flung his right arm round Bannister's shoulders, his left round Martin's. "You're going back to your ship, to-day," he announced. "Come with me."

The soldiers with whom they had been living for so long followed them out of the house into the front garden and crowded round them and said good-bye in Chinese. Some came forward to shake hands.

A private, who spoke English well, said, "We are sorry to see you go. We will all miss you very much." The cook, with whom Martin had become quite friendly, and who used to give him extra sweets, a tall, husky Manchurian who smiled a great deal, said something to them in Chinese which they did not understand. It was one o'clock in the afternoon. Bannister and Martin said good-bye and piled into the back of the lorry with Major Yan.

The Major pulled a piece of paper out of his pocket and gave it to Bannister. On it was written:

We are returning Stoker Bannister and Boy-seaman Martin, two members of the crew of H.M.S. *Amethyst*, owing to the fact that there have always been good relations between China and England.

"That," Yan said, "is for your captain. Be sure to give it to him." Bannister said that he would.

The lorry rolled carefully along the rough road that hugged the river. Presently it climbed up a small hill, and from the crown Bannister and Martin could see a naval vessel anchored in the river.

There she was. There was *Amethyst*.

"There doesn't seem to be much damage from here," Bannister said. "Do you suppose they did some repair-work while we were gone?"

Martin grinned. "Don't she look wonderful, Paddy? Don't she look terrific?" For him this was a long and moving speech.

The lorry stopped in a tiny village, and the two were taken into a cottage and told to sit down and wait. The woman of the cottage brought them tea.

Bannister proudly exhibited a bit of his recently acquired Chinese.

"*She-she*," he said. "Thank you."

It was just after two o'clock when the Major came in, still smiling and friendly.

"One of your officers has landed to take you back to the ship with him," he said. Then Lieutenant Hett came through the door. Bannister and Martin stood to attention.

"Glad to see you both," Hett said. His boyish face was shining.

"Glad to see you, sir," Bannister said. He had never meant anything so much.

"How did they treat you?"

"Very well, sir."

Hett took them back to the ship. The entire ship's company was on the quarterdeck to greet them.

Winfield, one of Bannister's friends, boomed in his deep voice, "H'ya, Paddy! Are you okay, lad?"

Bannister grinned. "I'm fine, mate. Just fine."

Boy-seaman Bernard Shaw came over and thumped Martin on the back. "Gosh, I'm sure glad to see you again, Keith. We thought you were dead. One of the other fellows was killed early on, see. Messed about, he was. And when you didn't show up we thought it was you."

"That so?" Martin said.

He wasn't much of a one for talking, but it was good to get back to the ship. It certainly was.

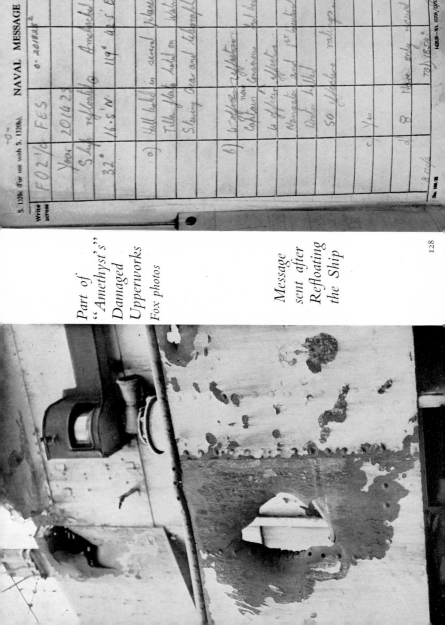

Part of
"Amethyst's"
Damaged
Upperworks
Fox photos

Message
sent after
Refloating
the Ship

Scarred and battered,
"Amethyst" reaching Safe
Harbour

Photo Keystone

129

Chapter Twenty-three

BARTER

Soon after the Communist crossings of the Yangtse, when it became apparent that *Amethyst* might have to remain up the river for some time, McCarthy and Griffiths set about to take stock of the food-supplies on board the ship. They found that certain foods, particularly fresh vegetables, would soon be running short. They counted the potatoes, and found that there were only enough left for forty-three meals.

"We'll have to begin rationing right away, Chef," McCarthy said, shaking his head. "We'll have to do that at least until we know more definitely what's going to happen to us about that safe-conduct. We may be up here a long time, and we can't take any chances on our food."

On the 4th of May, when Kerans returned from one of his meetings with the Communists on shore, he called McCarthy into the small office next to the chartroom which he had taken over as his private cabin.

"Oh, Stores P.O.," Kerans said, almost casually, "I've arranged for some traders to come out to the ship with a list of the foodstuffs they can supply for us. See what you can do with them, will you?"

"Very good, sir."

"I'm afraid Hong Kong money will be of no use. You'll have to try bartering with them."

McCarthy said that he would do what he could.

Next day the traders arrived in the side-party sampan. Hett met them on the quarterdeck. Since they could speak no English, the Captain's steward, But Sai Tin, a chubby, mournful Chinese, once again acted as interpreter.

Hett sent for McCarthy, who came at once. "Here are the

I 129

traders," Hett said. "See what they've got and what they'll take as barter."

"Yes, sir."

The No. 1 trader was a fat little man who wore a trilby at an incongruously jaunty angle. McCarthy later learned that he was the most important man in the near-by village of Ma-chia-shaw, on the south shore of the Yangtse, but since the village consisted only of a small brick kiln and a dozen houses made of stone with straw roofs, this did not signify a great deal.

The No. 1 trader's assistant was a small man, unhealthy-looking and obviously a sceptic concerning the virtue of bathing. He had snooping, busy eyes, and his sour expression never varied.

"What have you got for sale?" McCarthy asked the No. 1 trader. But Sai Tin translated.

The No. 1 trader bobbed his head up and down, grinning without humour. "Eggs and cabbages," he said. He looked McCarthy over carefully, and then, as if he had seen enough, transferred his attention to where the land rose in a gradual slope behind his village, until, in the distance, it developed into a respectable range of rolling hills.

This apparent lack of interest was deceptive. McCarthy had heard that the Chinese love to bargain. Now he was to discover that this report was quite correct.

"What will you give me," the trader offered as an unexpected opening gambit, "for ten dozen eggs?"

This sudden directness caught McCarthy unawares. "What do you want for them?" he said.

The trader looked at him, with, McCarthy thought, a trace of pity, as if he considered McCarthy not up to the bartering standard he usually met. "What are you going to give me?" the trader tossed back.

Obviously it was up to McCarthy to make the initial bid. He plunged. "Twenty pounds of sugar." He had no idea if, on the prevailing Chinese market, this was too much or two little.

"One hundred pounds of sugar would be a fair price," the trader said, without changing his expression.

"For that you can keep your eggs," McCarthy said; but he knew that he was in a tight spot. The trader was obviously aware that he would have to buy in the end. Food on board could not last for ever, and, except for certain staples, it was running low already. Thus McCarthy's bargaining position was anything but strong.

The trader, standing silently, looked at McCarthy and waited. McCarthy said nothing, holding his ground. Then the trader began to talk in rapid, fluid Chinese, waving his arms about and spitting a little as he talked.

"What does he say?" McCarthy asked after a while.

"He says you can't have his eggs at that price." But Sai Tin shrugged his shoulders. "He says that is giving the eggs away for nothing."

McCarthy's lips thinned. "Thirty pounds of sugar."

There was another long harangue in Chinese. Then: "He says, no, he can't do it. He says, don't you want to buy any eggs from him? He says, it is a waste of his time to come out to the ship."

"My last offer," McCarthy said, "is forty pounds of sugar. Take it or leave it." He turned and began to walk away, slowly, worrying even as he did so whether or not he was taking too big a risk. The Chinese steward called after him.

"He says forty-five!"

McCarthy turned. He walked back, trying to wear an expression as impassive as the trader's. "All right," he said, secretly relieved. "Ask him if it is possible to get anything else besides eggs and cabbages."

After a further exchange in Chinese But Sai Tin reported: "He says he'll let you know. He says he'll be back this afternoon with the eggs, and he will tell you then."

The traders left. They did not return that day, and McCarthy thought, with a feeling of mild panic, that he had bid too low after all, and the traders would not return in spite of the apparent agreement. At ten o'clock the next morning, however, the No. 1 trader turned up, grinning his bald, humourless grin.

"Why are you so late with your delivery?" McCarthy scolded.

The trader looked surprised. "I am not late," he said. "I had to go to Chingkiang to collect the eggs."

For a while McCarthy gave the traders small orders from day to day, feeling sure that *Amethyst* would not be in her fix for long. The No. 1 trader, however, was not in favour of day-to-day bartering. He complained with some bitterness that since all his supplies had to come down the fifteen miles from Chingkiang by rickshaw, and since the cost of rickshaw transport was heavy, it was unreasonable to continue doing business that way. Eventually McCarthy agreed to give him orders on a weekly basis instead.

Fresh vegetables were now coming to the ship fairly regularly. Griffiths was getting potatoes—which were scarce along the Yangtse that season—eggs, cabbages, onions, turnips, and vegetable marrow from the traders, and with these he was able to offer the men a reasonably varied menu.

As the weeks wore on and McCarthy began to place less and less of his confidence in the eventual grant of a safe-conduct by the Communists, the No. 1 trader succeeded in pushing his bids higher and higher. Sometimes the bargaining sessions lasted for as long as two and a half hours, with McCarthy beating a slow but sure strategic retreat and the No. 1 trader pressing him harder all the time.

The basic price for eggs soon shot up to a hundred pounds of sugar for ten dozen. Sixty catties of potatoes—a catty being a Chinese weight equal to one and one-tenth pounds—cost the exorbitant barter price of fifty pounds of sugar, plus one hundred pounds of flour.

McCarthy saw that at this rate it was only a question of time before *Amethyst's* stocks of sugar and flour would become too scarce to use as barter goods.

"What will we eat then?" McCarthy thought.

Chapter Twenty-four

THE PATIENTS

Long, long ago (it now seemed), when the wounded were being loaded into the flotilla of sampans to be evacuated from the ship, Brynley Howell, the stores assistant, had come to Frank with a plea. He had a small wound in his cheek.

"They want to take me off with the ones that are really wounded," Howell protested to Frank. "This thing on my cheek is hardly anything at all. Can't I stay on board, Les? Can't you fix it up so as I can stay?"

"I don't know, mate," Frank said, wanting to help. "Come along with me, and we'll check with the doc." The two found Fearnley busy with the more seriously wounded down on the mess-deck. He was giving them last-minute shots of morphia and penicillin before they were loaded into the sampans for, he thought, the hospital at Chingkiang.

Frank said, "Sorry to trouble you, sir, but this man has been told to leave the ship with the wounded, and he would like to remain on board. He's got a splinter in his cheek. What do you think, sir? Ought he to stay?"

Fearnley briefly examined Howell.

"I don't see why he can't stay if he wants to," he said. "It's only a minor wound."

Soon after the wounded had gone Howell, a quiet young man from Haverfordwest, came to see Fearnley again. The doctor treated the wound in his cheek. Then Howell had surprised Fearnley, rather pleasantly, by asking, "Can I be your sick-berth assistant, sir? I've always been kind of interested in that sort of thing."

Fearnley had no assistant at the time. "I'll be glad to give you a trial," he said.

Later he was glad that Howell had remained on board. The Welshman had pitched right into his new work with extraordinary adaptability. He soon learned to follow Fearnley's instructions, even to giving injections with a hypodermic syringe. He had tidied up the sick bay so that, in a few days, it was free of debris and back in use. Altogether Howell had become an invaluable medical aide.

At about half-past four one afternoon early in June Boy Sidney Horton, a seventeen-year-old lad from Leicestershire, was busily at work on the cable deck. He had been assigned to adjust the boom that kept the cable from scraping against the ship's bow. He was not later able to explain exactly how it had happened, but somehow a taut cable had pounced on his right arm, slapping against it with lightning force.

He heard something snap, crisp as a piece of iced celery, and suddenly there was no feeling in his arm. Looking down, he saw that already his right elbow had begun to swell. A few moments later it seemed twice its normal size.

Horton left his job and made his way to the sick bay. He asked Howell to look at his injury. Howell did. He pursed his lips.

"I'd better fetch the quack down to have a good look at that," Howell said, meaning no slight to Fearnley. He brought the doctor down, and Fearnley examined the arm and elbow, feeling along it with careful, exploring fingers.

"Does it hurt much?" he asked.

"Some," Horton admitted. He was sweating freely. He was clenching and unclenching his good hand. "It didn't at first, but it's beginning to be pretty bad now."

"I'll see what I can do for you," Fearnley said. "First I'm going to put you to sleep." He gave Horton an injection, and presently the boy was completely under its influence. While he was asleep, Fearnley put the damaged arm into a plaster cast.

Next day Horton complained that the cast was bothering him a great deal. It was too tight, he said. Upon examining it Fearnley saw that the broken arm had swollen still more, and that the cast was now too small. He broke the cast off, carefully, and had Electrical Artificer Lionel Chare make Horton an experimental cast out of copper.

"Is that better?" Fearnley asked him.

"I don't think it is, sir," Horton said, shaking his head. "It doesn't seem to give me any support. My arm is all kind of loose in it."

Fearnley removed the copper casing, and instead put Horton's arm in a simple sling. Then the break began to mend.

The sun shone, beating down on the deck of the ship. Heat waves rose, shimmering, from the surface of the Yangtse, distorting the land behind them, dancing their mad, almost invisible dance of satanic glee. The whole world seemed to throb and pulsate with the heat. Fearnley, stubbornly taking his daily constitutional round the upper deck, tried to ignore the heat, but he was not being very successful at it. He had begun to gain weight, and the added roll round his middle was beginning to worry him.

Garns called to him from the ship's rail.

"I think Cheesi would like you to take a look at her baby, sir," he said. Garns' voice sounded limp and lazy with the melting heat.

Fearnley sighed, giving up all thoughts of continuing his walk. He strolled slowly to the side of the ship, partly surrendering himself to the sun. He looked over the side, and saw that the Chinese girl was holding her baby up appealingly in her arms.

She said something in her own language that didn't mean anything to Fearnley, but her gesture was unmistakable.

Kerans, his face glistening with perspiration and beginning to burn, strolled by.

"You might as well look the child over, Doc.," he said. "Since the sampan women are our only contact with shore, I think it would help create a good feeling if you did what you could to help them." Kerans had a young daughter at home.

He often thought of her now, in this grim period of negotiating with the Communists and waiting hopefully for the safe-passage down the river.

"All right," Fearnley said, "if you say so."

He had Cheesi helped on board with her baby. He soon found that the child had an infection in her right eye which obviously required attention, but which had not yet become serious. He treated the infection.

Next day he treated it again. Soon, responding to his attentions, the infection had quite vanished. The eye was clear and healthy.

Cheesi was as delighted as she was impressed with Fearnley's quick cure. Perhaps she was too impressed, Fearnley thought the next day, for when she came out in the sampan this time she brought her husband with her. She asked the doctor to make him well, as he had done for their child.

He was a small, fever-plagued Chinese, hollow-cheeked and scrawny. When he stripped for an examination Fearnley saw that his ribs pushed out against his drum-tight skin as if they were trying to burst free. It soon became clear that he was suffering from chronic malaria.

For several days Fearnley treated him. When he was eventually dismissed he told Fearnley gratefully, through But Sai Tin, that he was a new man.

"He says he feel very good," the steward explained. "Better than for years."

Cheesi's husband bobbed his head and smiled, as if he understood every word. Then, to Fearnley's surprise, he thrust a basket full of eggs into the doctor's hand. This, he made clear, was for services rendered. He bowed low and departed.

Even that was only the beginning.

Next day the sampan brought Midnight's husband out to see the doctor as well. His complaint was a series of small but painful tumours just under his skin. Fearnley began to wonder if Kerans' policy of neighbourliness had not, after all, been a mistake.

"I'm going to give you a local anæsthetic," Fearnley explained to him through the steward. "You won't feel anything but one quick jab."

His patient nodded agreeably. Obviously, after the good reports that had come to him from the female crew of the sampan, he was confident that the young Royal Air Force doctor could do no wrong. He took his clothes off on Fearnley's instructions and stretched out with complete confidence at full length on the operating-table. Fearnley punched the needle home. He released the local anæsthetic.

He had barely withdrawn the hypo when Mr Midnight, grinning with relief and pleasure, hopped off the table. He bowed low and reached for his trousers.

"What the hell's going on here?" Fearnley demanded, astonished. He grabbed the Chinese and pushed him back on to the table. There was a flood of unintelligible protest.

But Sai Tin interrupted with a faint smile. "He feel the jab, and you say he feel no more; so he think it all over."

Soon after this Fearnley's uninvited panel of Chinese civilian patients was further augmented when the No. 1 trader, who had heard of Fearnley's apparently spectacular success, first with the baby and then with the two husbands of the sampan girls, reported to him with an ulcer on his back. He asked Fearnley for treatment, which he received. In return he paid the doctor with a basket of duck eggs and a live duck.

That afternoon Kerans stepped out into the sun from the wireless office. He rubbed his eyes, refusing for a moment to believe them. He looked again.

Yes, it was true. Stoker Mechanic Charles Hawkins, clad only in underpants, was marching round the deck sporting a self-congratulatory smirk. In his right hand he carried the end of a piece of string. At the other end of the string waddled a live, protestingly quacking duck.

Later, when he told Hett about it, Kerans remarked, "You don't often see a sight like that in one of His Majesty's ships!" The corners of his mouth kept climbing upward as he thought of it. For one thing, how could he doubt that the morale of the men was anything but sound when they still had the high spirits to try a thing like that?

He felt light-hearted for quite a while after that—even if Fearnley did not. The following day, when the doctor went down to the sick bay, he found a long line of Chinese waiting for treatment—men, women, and children.

"That does it," Fearnley decided. "If this thing keeps growing I won't be able to give the ship's company the attention they need to keep them in good health." He called for But Sai Tin.

"Tell the sampan girls," he said, "that from now on we've got a brand-new house rule. Relatives okay. Friends, absolutely no."

More than two weeks after Horton had broken his arm Kerans came back to the ship from a meeting with Kang. He reported to Fearnley that the Chinese Colonel had, out of the blue, insisted on making the point that he and his Government had no quarrel with the men of *Amethyst*.

"He says it wasn't our men but the British Government which was at fault," Kerans said, smiling. "But he also said he would be glad to provide medical facilities or anything else that might be needed for the comfort and health of the ship's company. Have you any ideas?"

"We ought to try them out on that one," Fearnley said, "to see if they mean what they say. Let's ask Kang if I can take Horton to the hospital at Chingkiang to have his arm X-rayed. He's well on the mend, anyhow, but it'll do as a test."

Kerans pursed his lips. "Why not?" he concurred, after a moment's thought. "I can't see any harm in it." At the next meeting he made Fearnley's request to Kang.

The following day Kang sent a jeep to take Horton and Fearnley to the hospital. The X-ray was taken.

Then the jeep took them back along the makeshift road to a point near the ship. They returned to *Amethyst* in the sampan.

"Hey, Sid," Petty Officer Samuel Logan asked Horton,

"were there any good women aboard the hospital?" The men clustered round him.

"Sure," Horton grinned. He was seventeen years old, but he was just under six feet tall and looked more mature than his years. "The only trouble was I didn't even get a chance to talk to them."

Chapter Twenty-five

SAFE-CONDUCT?

Most of Kerans' meetings with the Communists were held at Chingkiang, which was a large river town with narrow streets which, leaning rather too heavily on its past glories and rather too lightly on riding along with the times, had in recent years gone somewhat to seed.

Getting from the ship to Chingkiang meant making use of various forms of transport, as the journey could not be made all in a single stage. The first short step in the fifteen-mile trip was, of course, in the sampan-ferry across the scudding current of the Yangtse to the south bank. The current tugged at the sampan, nagging it downstream, so that it approached the shore several hundred yards below the ship. Then the female crew propelled it upstream again, along the edge of the river, where the current lost its battle with the firm bank, and, when they reached a point opposite the ship, beached the flat-bottomed craft.

From the landing-point a Communist soldier, always at that post, escorted Kerans to the local garrison headquarters in the near-by village from which Captain Tai-ko Liang and his troop kept a constantly watchful guard on the ship. There the Captain became Kerans' personal bodyguard, sticking to him leechlike as he escorted him on foot along a winding path for the twenty-five minutes it took to walk to the road. Then an American-made staff car picked them up and drove them in to Chingkiang for the meeting.

The headquarters building in which the meetings were held was near the centre of the city. Built of grey stone, it had walls of at least a foot in thickness, which, with the help of cross-ventilation from its high windows, made the interior pleasantly cool even during the intensely hot and dusty days of summer. This was one of the most imposing houses in the town; and it was further marked for distinction by fresh, green garlands and, in a place of supreme honour over the main entrance to the courtyard, a huge photograph, several times larger than life, of the rotund and smiling face of Communist leader Mao Tse-tung.

The meetings were held, in what was once a banqueting-hall, round a table that was twenty feet or more in length.

On his arrival the first thing Kerans was offered was a hot, clean towel. With this he mopped his face, his brow, his hands. Hot Chinese tea was then served, before the meeting began, in white cups which had no handles, which were filled at frequent intervals and never allowed to become completely empty. While he waited for each meeting to begin Kerans paced up and down the room, impatiently puffing at a cigarette.

At most of these meetings—Kerans attended eleven in all—Colonel Kang was the senior Communist officer present, but General Yuan Chung-hsien, the fifty-year-old Chinkiang Area Commander, did attend on three occasions. Yuan was obviously well-educated; his manners were impeccable; his uniform, of a slightly darker shade of green than those worn by the others, and of a better cut than most, carried no badge of rank. He, like Mao, was a native of Honan Province.

Kang, on the other hand, had been a successful Peking lawyer. His close-cropped hair, very dark, even for a Chinese, covered a bullet head. Kerans gathered after many long dis cussions that he, unlike some of his fellow-officers in t Chinese People's Liberation Army, was completely devo to the Communist cause.

Kang almost invariably delayed his own arrival meetings until Kerans had been waiting for some n Then he burst into the room in a rush with his two inte a Captain Jen and another officer whose name Ker heard mentioned. Kerans shook hands all round, later said, "We would then stand and suck t another. Then we would sit round the big tabl chair at the head vacant in case the General should come. I always removed my cap. They kept theirs on."

Quite often at these meetings the Communist Press and Propaganda Section was represented by a pale, sickly little man who looked quite out of place in uniform. What his exact function was Kerans was never sure, but he was usually accompanied by a rather pretty Chinese woman, in her mid-twenties, who kept taking pictures by the dozen with a Leica. Nothing escaped her lens.

The meetings lasted anything from one to four hours. During the longer sessions there was usually a break for tea and cakes and sugared almonds, and, at the last get-together, Kang surprised Kerans completely by giving him a six-course lunch. "I would like to know who paid for it," Kerans remarked to Strain on the way back to the ship.

Gradually, as these discussions went on and Kerans saw that agreement was just as far away as it had ever been, he formed the impression that Kang was simply stalling for reasons of his own. The Communist Colonel made a point on each separate occasion of telling Kerans, "If you move the ship every effort be made to destroy it. If you do not all will be well."

men on board *Amethyst* clung optimistically to the arly weeks of the ship's imprisonment up the safe-conduct would eventually be granted. May, the watchful men of the Communist enough to look like green bugs, released fire across the bow of the ship. There it.

doesn't get too rough with them for ll seriousness. "We don't want to he ought to wait until we get back te Kang a strong letter of protest." ar the remark. "At least," he imistic."

in the former banqueting-hall in Chingkiang. One Saturday in mid-June, Kerans had a message from Kang suggesting a meeting for the following morning. This was quite satisfactory to *Amethyst's* captain: he had had a message over the wireless advising him that some bags of mail for the ship's crew were being held up by the Communists in Shanghai, and he was glad now of the opportunity of asking Kang to expedite its delivery.

Kerans had fallen into the comfortable pattern of asking one of *Amethyst's* petty officers or key ratings to accompany him to each meeting—a different man each time. He did this for two good reasons: first, as a means of keeping the ship's company informed about the meetings, and thus maintaining morale; and, second, for the feeling of solid support it gave him to have a member of his own team with him when he visited the Communists on *their* home ground.

He sent for McCarthy. "Stores Petty Officer," he asked, "would you like to come along with me to the meeting?" McCarthy said he would, indeed.

Next morning at half-past nine a Communist-manned motor-boat slid in alongside the ship and picked them up, taking them from there to the island of Chiao Shan, about three miles upstream. This was the same island Kerans had passed in the landing-craft on that day, now so long ago, when he had first boarded *Amethyst*.

McCarthy, approaching the island for the first time, saw the gold-and-white temple sitting on the pyramid-shaped hill. At first the sun, reflecting brightly from the golden dome, dazzled him. He wondered, for a while, if the meeting was to be held in the temple, but soon learned that it was not. Instead, it was held in the messroom of a stone barracks not far from shore, which had been abandoned by the Nationalist Navy. It was a solid, two-storey structure, with a wide veranda facing the south bank of the river.

This time there was no waiting for the Communists to arrive. McCarthy and Kerans were met stiffly at the door by Colonel Kang—who immediately impressed McCarthy as a kind of Chinese-Prussian, militaristic and strict and unwaveringly serious—and by Kang's team of interpreters, propagandists, and advisers.

The two Britons shook hands politely with the Chinese and sat down to the usual preliminary tea, this time served at once, together with sugared almonds and fancy cakes. McCarthy took the setting in with painstaking care, recording his impressions on his memory, so that he could pass them on to the ship's company when he returned. The woman photographer from the Press and Propaganda Department was there, and she pounced on McCarthy with her Leica, as she always did on a new face from *Amethyst*, like a greedy bird of prey. She shot pictures of him from all angles, while somewhat nervously he munched sugared almonds. McCarthy could not help wondering into what vast collection of dossiers the pictures would go, and what use would be made of them. "I pretended not to notice her," McCarthy told Griffiths when he returned to the ship, "but I have to admit it was distracting."

Kerans had long since learned that any request he wished to make of the Communists at these meetings had to be presented in the form of a written memorandum. (During the eleven meetings he handed in a grand total of sixty-three such memoranda, most of which were ignored.) He delivered to Kang a formal note requesting that the mail be forwarded from Shanghai. Kang, whose impassive reception of such requests seemed to indicate that he neither spoke nor read English, turned the memorandum over to Captain Jen without so much as glancing at it himself. Jen translated it into Chinese for his benefit.

Kang shrugged his shoulders. He spoke at some little length to Jen, who then turned to Kerans.

"My Colonel says he is agreeable regarding the delivery of mail——"

"Ah, good!" Kerans breathed.

"——but you will have to get permission from Shanghai as well."

"And how do I get that?"

There was no reply beyond a shrug.

When Kerans and McCarthy returned to the ship Kerans hurried to the wireless office. He asked French to send a message to the British authorities in Shanghai telling them that he now had on-the-spot permission for the delivery of the mail if they could arrange to have it sent on from their end. He didn't think there was much chance that the Communists would actually let the mail through, but he felt he could lose nothing by trying.

At noon on June the 22nd Kerans sent a message down to Williams, who was off duty in the engineroom artificers' mess. The message read:

E.R.A. Williams from Captain

I would like yourself or E.R.A. McGlashen to accompany me ashore for a meeting with Colonel Kang. Be ready by 1500 hours this afternoon.

This meeting was at Chingkiang. It was noteworthy as one of the exceptional few attended by General Yuan.

Williams, totally without experience in dealing with the Communists, was hardly able to contain his joy when Yuan suggested to Kerans that he should obtain a written agreement from Admiral Sir Patrick Brind, the British Naval Commander-in-Chief, Far East Station, to appoint a British representative who would continue discussions in Chingkiang after *Amethyst* was granted a free passage. Williams was sure that this would mean an early departure down the river to freedom for the ship, which had now been anchored under the Communist guns for two full months.

At this meeting Kang, who had apparently had word from Shanghai, promised the delivery of the mail, and also of certain stores and medical supplies. It all looked wonderfully promising to Williams.

When he reboarded *Amethyst* the men grouped eagerly around him for news of the meeting and of the safe-conduct.

"What happened, mate? Give us the gen."

Williams told them about the General's reference to the safe-passage. During this quiet period it took very little to spread a rumour through the ship, especially a rumour of a hoped-for early departure. Sometimes one was conjured out of thin air. Therefore it did not take long for Williams' report to be picked up by the ship's company. As the report spread, naturally it also grew.

Shortly after Williams had returned Freeman joined Frank in the petty officers' mess.

"Heard the news, Les?"

"What news?"

"Why, that we'll be leaving on Wednesday for sure," Freeman said, "with a safe-passage."

"Ha!" Frank snorted.

"It's true, Les."

"I'll believe *that* when the captain tells it, not before."

"But it's all round the ship. Everybody knows about it except you."

One by one other members of the ship's company came to Frank with the same story. He steadfastly refused to consider it seriously.

"Have you heard we're leaving, Frankie?"

"I've heard it," Frank said. "I don't have to believe it."

And later: "Any truth in the buzz that we're going, Les?"

"Not as far as I'm concerned," Frank said.

At about five o'clock that afternoon Kerans, strolling round the upper deck, overheard two of his men still animatedly talking about the impending departure as if it were an established fact. "This isn't good," he thought.

He collected the ship's company together on the after mess-deck.

"I've heard a rumour running round the ship," he said, frowning, his long face impressively serious, "that we're supposed to be going down-river in a couple of days with a safe-passage. I wish it were true. Unfortunately there's nothing in it; nothing at all." He paused, taking in the disappointed faces around him. "I want you to know that if anything *is* going to happen I'll let you know in plenty of time."

During the long, sweltering wait, with the temperature pushing unmercifully upward each day, the men thought of many things. Frank, whose last shore home had been in Hull, often wondered how Hull City had finished up in the Second Division. He thought of Kathleen, his Irish wife, and of Leslie junior, who was eighteen. He thought of Pearl, his nine-year-old daughter, and of the baby, David, not yet three.

He scribbled figures down on paper and added them up, and discovered, somewhat to his surprise, that in the past twenty years he had been home with his family for a total of five of them; and he wondered if he would ever see Kathleen and the children again. When he got down to bed-rock with himself he had to admit that he saw very little hope of getting out of the Yangtse alive. He could see no improvement in *Amethyst's* position—he felt that the opposite was true—and he could see no possible happy solution. He had complete faith in Kerans, but, he often asked himself, how could anyone accomplish anything worthwhile so long as the Communists refused to co-operate?

He wondered if young Leslie would be capable of looking after the family if anything should happen to *Amethyst* and himself, and whether, in such an unhappy event, the Royal Marines would release his eldest son from service on compassionate grounds, so that he could keep the home going.

Sometimes the older members of the crew—men like Jack Walker, who was twenty-eight—thought about their own behaviour, and of how important it was to set a good example for the many teen-aged seamen aboard.

The long, empty wait was hard on the nerves. "I've got to keep steady because of the kids," Walker thought. He was reasonably sure that if anything happened to start the Communists firing at the ship again the ship would have to fight back—even if every man aboard was killed. He too wondered if he'd ever see his home town—Birmingham—again.

Sometimes, sitting out on the deck after dark, he played a little game all by himself, a very personal little game. He would pick out a specific star in the sky. He would call the star Betty, and he would think, "Well, if I see Betty again to-morrow night that will be fine."

That was the way he lived—for to-day and perhaps for to-morrow, but not worrying unduly about to-morrow. It was like that with most of the ship's company. They did not lose their optimism, except now and then, rarely, for short periods, and they always looked to the next meeting Kerans would have with the Communists as a possible release from their growing difficulties. There, perhaps waiting for them like a distant prize, was always the chance of a safe-passage down the Yangtse, so that they could get back into the safe bosom of the fleet.

Chapter Twenty-six

MAIL

It was about five in the afternoon, and William Garfitt and Hartness were playing Ludo—Uckers in the Navy—on the after mess-deck. They had been playing, off and on, all the long weeks since the action. Secretly they were beginning to tire of tossing the dice and advancing their men round the zigzag track, but they did not put their boredom into words. What other way could they find to kill unending time?

Hartness, suddenly remembering the forty or more gramophone records on board the ship which had not been played since Hong Kong, stopped in the act of shaking the dice for another throw.

"Say, Fish," he said, "I've got an idea. A pretty good one. What do you say we put on some of those records over the S.R.E.[1] with spoken introductions?"

"Stretch it out a little, Scouse. What do you mean?"

"Well, we could play request numbers for everybody, see, from the captain down. What d'you say?"

"Why not?" Garfitt thought about it for a moment. "You know, it's got possibilities. Maybe we could pull a few legs. You and me can be the masters of ceremonies, huh?"

'That's the idea, Fish. I s'pose we'd better ask the captain for his okay."

The two men, leaving their unfinished game, went to ask Kerans for his permission to broadcast, as planned, over the ship's recording equipment. Kerans, who believed that anything that might help morale was a good idea, quickly assented. That evening between six o'clock and seven they went on.

Hartness, as the originator of the scheme, introduced the

[1] S.R.E. = ship's relaying equipment.

149

first number. He had made his choice carefully, and he wondered how it would be received by the men.

"This song," he announced cheerfully, "comes to the ship's company with all good wishes from the after mess-deck." He lowered the needle carefully.

The number, a recording by the Ink Spots, blared out over the ship. What the Ink Spots harmonized was a ditty entitled *Don't ask us when we're Leaving*.

The Communists were always there, with their eyes on *Amethyst* and their guns pointed at her; and the men on the ship knew it. They could feel the eyes, even when they couldn't actually see them, and they could feel the uncomfortable threat of the guns.

One evening in June Winfield, Hawkins, Brown, and George Maddocks were lounging about on the quarterdeck, singing songs that reminded them nostalgically of home, and then falling silent for a while. After a spell they would snap out of their unaccustomed quiet mood by joking and laughing and pulling one another's legs. Then they returned to singing their homesick songs. This was often their programme of an evening, just standing about and singing, and making quips and smoking.

At about ten o'clock, when it had become quite dark, Winfield snapped a match alight against his thumbnail and applied it to the end of a fresh cigarette. He inhaled once, deeply, and released the smoke in a thick cloud, and suddenly the pleasant quiet of the night was spoiled by the nasty, menacing whine of a bullet, and, a split second later, the sharp crack of a rifle. The shot was well over their heads, but the men were taking no chances. Soon the deck was quite bare.

Down on the mess-deck Winfield grumbled, "Them Commies are getting to be real show-offs. They just wanted to show us who's boss."

"G'way," Maddocks snorted. "The Chinks don't like us at all; that's the trouble. I bet they think a good Englishman is a dead Englishman."

The stokers brooded over the incident. They were glad, of course, that the shot had passed high overhead, but, in an obscure way, this calculated miss began to rankle as an insult. Winfield and Hawkins, particularly, tried to think of some way to take vengeance. A few evenings later they hit upon an idea which satisfied them.

They borrowed a boiler-suit from the engineroom and stuffed it up with rags to look like a guy—complete with boots and gloves and a pillow for a head. While there was still plenty of daylight they took it up to the quarterdeck, near the ship's bell and in full view of the shore.

They waited until a group of Communist soldiers had gathered to watch them from the shore. Then Winfield pinned a cardboard sign on the dummy's chest. It read simply, in large block letters (which, incidentally, it was probably fortunate the Chinese could not read), MAO TSE-TUNG.

Hawkins cleared his throat ponderously. He pronounced sentence on the guy.

"Mr Mao Tse-tung," he said, "we find you guilty of crimes against the British Navy, and sentence you to hang by the neck until you are dead."

He fastened a rope round the neck of the guy, and threw the other end of the rope over the crosspiece that held the ship's bell. Then he pulled on the rope and tied it in place, with the effigy of Mao swinging easily in the light breeze.

Winfield, also mock-solemn, said, "And may God have mercy on your soul." Then he added, "If you've got one."

It seemed to give the men a kind of release.

Later that night Hawkins said, "I guess we better take old Mao down, huh?"

"Why not leave him up there for a while, mate?" Winfield said. "Alf White hasn't seen him yet." He winked knowingly.

"I don't get it," Hawkins said.

Winfield explained. "Old Alf's not very fond of the dark, see? What do you think he'll say if he comes along making his rounds and suddenly runs into old Mao?"

Hawkins chuckled, and the chuckle developed into a laugh,

and the laugh became a roar. When he calmed down there were tears in his eyes. He wiped them away with the back of his hand. "Lovely," he said. "That's really a very lovely idea."

They left the dummy hanging from the bell and hid and watched it. An hour later, not so sure that it had been a good idea, they were still there. White had not shown up. Soon afterwards, feeling flat at their failure to frighten their shipmate, they untied the rope and lowered the effigy and took it apart and went to bed.

"Anyway," Winfield said, "we showed them Chinks they can't fool around with us."

The men soon realized that boredom was their worst enemy—even deadlier in its way than the uniformed, armed troops watching them from shore. In addition to the games they played—cards, Monopoly, Ludo—they were happy for the variety to a dull existence given by the shipboard screenings. Fortunately the projector and the seven feature-length films had not been seriously injured in the shelling. The ship carried three operators—Electrician Blomley, Electrician's Mate George Paul, and Electrician Vernon Irwin—but Blomley had by now become one of French's wireless assistants, and Paul was kept busy in the engineroom. This left Irwin to handle the screenings, which began, after the April action, at the ambitious rate of one every evening. After it became evident that the stay up-river might be prolonged, performances were reduced, first to alternate nights, and then, much later, to two shows weekly, and eventually to one.

The films were run through in strict rotation, usually on a Sunday evening down in the seamen's mess-deck, from which the light would not be visible to the watchers on shore. When the weather became stiflingly hot the crowding into this relatively small space made the atmosphere even more fetid, but the men seemed to think that the privilege of watching the shadows on the screen made it well worth the extra discomfort.

One of the films, *Twilight on the Rio Grande*, a Wild

Western epic starring Gene Autry and his horse, was attended at each successive showing by Chare, the acting schoolmaster. There is an incredible scene in the film which shows Autry, galloping at full speed after a bunch of crooks, bending down to scoop up a gun which one of them had dropped to the ground.

Irwin was curious about Chare's constant attendance at this particular film. "Hey, mate," he asked after one showing, "why do you always come back to see this one? What's it have that the others haven't?"

Chare grinned. "I'll tell you, Vern. I keep coming in the hope that our hero will miss picking up that damn' gun. He hasn't missed so far, has he?"

When it came to frolicking, the stokers always seemed to have the ideas. One afternoon when Ray was on watch on the bridge he heard shouts of glee from below-decks. "Some of the boys are up to something," he thought. Just then half a dozen men burst out on to the deck, some of them dressed as Red Indians in white shorts, sandals, and—authentic touch!—chicken feathers in their hair; others were supposed to be cowboys, with soft white sun-hats shaped to look like ten-gallon toppers and wooden six-guns they had carved out themselves. Bannister was one of the Indians, and all the participants in this typically North American game, usually played by small boys, were stokers and stoker mechanics.

"Bang!" shouted a cowboy. "Bang! Bang! Bang!" And another Redskin bit the dust. This went on for some time, with the corpses rising suddenly to their feet, whooping and hollering while the rest of the crew laughed at their crazy antics, and while Peggy, Griffiths' brown-and-white mongrel bitch, tore round after the stokers barking hysterically and joyously.

"I guess it was all damn-silly," Ray admitted later, "but it gave us all a laugh when laughs were few and far between. You had to hand it to them stokers for tomfoolery all right."

One morning, later in June, Ho You, the Chinese cook,

reported through Frank to Hett that five pounds of his money was missing. Hett reported the complaint to Kerans.

"Better search the Chinese mess," Kerans suggested. "Then we'll know what to do from there."

The Chinese mess was next door to the galley on the starboard side of the ship. There was a rather large shell-hole in the bulkhead, which had been blocked up with a mattress. Hett ordered each of the eight Chinese to spread his belongings out for a thorough search. They treated the order with calm indifference, spreading out their luggage without any trace of alarm as far as Hett could observe. But everything, he saw, was alive with cockroaches.

"Take this stuff out on to the quarterdeck at once and spray it," he ordered. He felt faintly ill. When the spraying had been completed Hett had the luggage gone through carefully, but the money was not found. Instead the search uncovered more than fifty tubes of penicillin and streptomycin, each tube worth more than five pounds in the black markets of Nanking.

"Whose stuff is this?" Hett demanded sternly. The drugs had obviously been purchased in Hong Kong, where they were relatively inexpensive, to be smuggled into China proper, where they were both rare and costly.

The Chinese, however, were adamant in their story: the drugs had not been smuggled aboard by any of them, but, perhaps, by one of the Chinese who had evacuated the ship in April. Who could tell for sure now which one of the evacuees it had been?

Obviously against this firm, collective stand Hett had no chance of uncovering the guilty man. After a while he gave up trying. There were more pressing matters to be dealt with.

Despite Kerans' pessimism, the mail arrived after all. It came, three bulging bags of it, on the 24th of June, after having been forwarded on, as promised, by the Communists from Shanghai.

Frank was awakened from a particularly sound sleep to sort

it out. He didn't mind. For the first time in seventy days this was direct news from home. But he reported to Kerans: "It looks to me as if this mail has been gone through on the way. It's been tampered with."

"Yes," Kerans agreed. "I rather expected that."

The word of the mail's delivery spread over the ship like the hot, searching breath of a flame-thrower. In a few minutes *Amethyst*, which had been so silent, echoed and re-echoed with excited shouts. Every man on board turned out of bed to read his mail from home.

McCarthy, near the head of the queue, took the letters and newspapers Frank gave him and retired to a reasonably quiet corner to read them. Three of the letters were from his wife, all written before the incident of April the 20th, and the latest of them post-marked April the 19th.

For a while silence fell over *Amethyst* again, while the men pored over their messages from Lewisham and Birr and Plymouth and Rhondda and Glasgow; from Dublin and Dunster; from Birmingham and West Hartlepool; from Leicester; from Liverpool; from Felixstowe and from Aberdeen; from all the corners of the British Isles. Then they gathered into bright-eyed, gesturing little groups and discussed what they had heard. McCarthy pointed to the black headlines on the front pages of the *News of the World* and *Sunday Empire News*, which had also come for him in the mail.

Freeman held up a newspaper he had received. He indicated a headline: NO-NAME HERO OF "AMETHYST." "It's all about Frenchie," he grinned. "He's going to like it when he finds he hasn't got any name."

"Well," McCarthy said, a little surprised, "it looks as if they've been thinking of us at home, after all!" He had, until then, shared the commonly accepted view held by Navy men that once one of them left the shores of Britain he was completely forgotten until he returned home again.

"That's a change for the people at home," Freeman said drily. "But look at the mess we had to get in before we got any notice."

All the same, he and McCarthy were secretly pleased. They had been stirred more than they cared to express by the arrival of the mail. Neither of them slept that night.

All over the ship, into the early hours, there was the restive, excited murmur of men discussing the news from home.

Chapter Twenty-seven

SNARE THE RAT

The days dragged on, heavy at times with tropical heat, drenched at others in tropical rain. From the end of May, when it became all too clear that his negotiations with the Communists for a safe-passage were likely to drag out, Kerans saw that it had become of truly vital importance to reduce fuel consumption. He shut the power off completely for longer and longer periods, until, a month after this rationing had begun, *Amethyst* had one power-less stretch which lasted for fifty-nine hours.

During such times the fans were still, leaving the ship humid and hot as an oven. Some nights the temperature below-decks reached a hundred and ten degrees. Quite a number of the men set camp-beds up on the quarterdeck in a vain effort to find coolness and sleep. Mostly they just sat about all night, wearing only a towel round the middle, or sometimes less, with sweat pouring ceaselessly down their bodies.

During the day, because of the lack of power and the accompanying lack of light, even the engineroom ratings worked on the upper deck. In the wireless office Rutter used an ancient bellows to cool French off while he transmitted messages, but even so, the wireless operator's fingers often slid off the wet, slippery key. When French transcribed incoming messages his sweat-soaked wrist stuck to the paper, making even that simple task incredibly annoying.

No machinery hummed. There was no pressure with which to flush the toilets, and fresh water had to be pumped up by hand when needed. Even the refrigeration was shut off, at the calculated risk of spoiling the remaining meat.

It was living in a dead ship.

The officers and ratings, accustomed to the steady, soothing hum of the motors, often caught themselves listening for the missing familiar sounds. The unaccustomed silences made them feel strangely on edge, and they listened uncomfortably to the noises it is not normal to hear on a live ship—echoing footsteps on steel decks, the scrape and click of rats' claws overhead, the sighing of the rigging in the wind, and the hollow voices, far away in another part of the ship, which should have been deadened by other sounds.

The rats had bred abnormally in the festering heat, and now they scurried round the ship, with growing confidence, by the hundred. Kerans became aware of this when he noticed that they had begun to eat the bindings of the books in the officers' cabin, now cleared of debris and used as their sleeping quarters.

"I've never seen that before," he said to Strain. "I mean, rats eating the bindings of books."

The ship had also become infested with ants, cockroaches, mosquitoes, and a tiny white moth, peculiar to the Yangtse, which flew in thick swarms and settled on everything, even dropping into the food. But the rats were the greatest menace. After a while it became unsafe to walk about in bare feet.

Simon, the ship's cat, managed to pounce on a few; Peggy was less successful; and traps were of no use at all. The men, however, trying every means that came to mind to catch and kill the big, furry rodents, occasionally had luck with home-made wire snares.

There was one particular wire-channel which ran along the roof of the after mess-deck that the rats liked to run along at night, scraping it metallically with their claws. It was a discomforting sound, and one that put sleep, already reluctant enough, still farther off.

A few of the men got together. Something, they decided, had to be done. One night they set a snare on the wire-channel.

Underneath Parnell had set up a complicated sleeping arrangement for himself, based on the hopeful premise that, for hot evenings when the power was off, it was a good idea to build his camp-bed up to the level of the portholes, where he would get any breeze that happened to be going. Accordingly he had pulled a mess-table out from near the bulkhead and had erected his camp-bed on it. What he did not know on this particular evening was that a rat-snare had been newly attached to the wire-channel just over his head.

It was about eleven o'clock when Parnell, more successful at wooing sleep than usual, was beginning to doze off. It was about eleven also when a large, red-eyed rat, running along the channel with its customary cockiness, poked his neck into the snare and was rudely stopped in its tracks. Suddenly there was the mad scratching and scrambling of furry, clawed feet and the frenzied twisting of a greasy and furry body. The snare tightened as the rat struggled, and presently it fell off the channel into space.

Squealing and instinctively redoubling its struggles, it kicked about in its death-throes. Now its hind legs were inches from Parnell's face. At first only faintly aware that some unusual movement was taking place near him, Parnell opened his eyes sleepily. Then he opened them wide.

"Hey!" he yelled.

Without pausing to consider his action, he twisted off the camp-bed. He landed on the table with a thump, bounced once, and landed, bruised and shaken, on the deck. Stunned, for a moment he lay there without moving.

Meanwhile one of the seamen had rushed for a pail of water, kept handy for just such an emergency. He held it under the rat while a shipmate cut the wire and ran out on to the deck to pour the strangling, drowning rat over the side.

Still shaken, Parnell crawled to his feet. He looked about, somewhat wildly, in the deep gloom. There was no sign of the rat where he had seen it, suspended unreasonably in mid-air.

"What's the matter, Parnell?" a voice, feigning sleepiness, asked. "Been having a nightmare?"

Chapter Twenty-eight

LESS IN THE LARDER

The meetings between Kerans and Kang continued at irregular intervals. The Communist Colonel seemed to take a deep and sadistic delight in raising Kerans' hopes at one meeting and then dashing them with great gusto at the next. The safe-passage for a long while seemed to bob up just ahead of Kerans, always promisingly close, but never quite within reach, like an electric hare before greyhounds. After a while he became more convinced than ever that Kang was leading him on, hoping that *Amethyst* would eventually have to give in for lack of both food and fuel. He had to admit to himself that Kang had every reason to believe, if this were his plan, that it would soon become reality.

Then, on the 1st of July, Kerans sent word to McCarthy that he wanted to see him. When the stores petty officer left the Captain's small cabin he was obviously downcast. He hurried to the galley to find Griffiths.

"I've just been talking to the captain, Chef," McCarthy announced dispiritedly. "He says we go on half-rations, beginning to-morrow."

Griffiths made no attempt to disguise his dismay. "My God, Jack, why, that's terrible!" To him this turn of events could mean only one thing: the skipper obviously now thought that *Amethyst* was stuck indefinitely up the Yangtse.

The word got round. The men discussed this new half-rations edict glumly. That evening Hartness announced a number over the S.R.E.

"This one," he said, "is dedicated to Colonel Kang, with no comment."

Then he played the record. It was *I've got you under my Skin.*

"*The Fat Men*"—*selected by Kerans*

The Chinese remaining after the Action

Gaping Holes from 75-mm. Shells

McCarthy and Griffiths together worked out how much flour was left on the ship and how long it could be made to last. The accuracy of their reckoning was remarkable: they calculated that they could stretch the flour out until the end of July. On the 31st of that month there was exactly one bag of flour left on board the ship.

Even on what technically passed for half-rations there was, however, sufficient food to keep the men going. This did not apply to Boy Dennis Roberts.

Roberts seemed never to have enough to eat. After the half-rations régime came into effect he called on Griffiths in the galley after every meal, looking miserable, and hungry.

"Got anything left, Chef?" he appealed. Griffiths went through the futile little ceremony of examining the pots for possible scrapings. His answer was almost always the same.

"Sorry, boy, not a thing."

Roberts slouched away, one hand caressing his unfilled stomach, thinking of the illustrated advertisements for food that kept taunting him from the pages of the *Saturday Evening Post*, *Collier's*, *MacLean's*, and other American and Canadian magazines which happened to be on board the ship.

Roberts' mates, well aware of his gigantic appetite, painstakingly went through the magazines for the most tempting illustrations. Rutter one evening found a particularly realistic full-colour advertisement of a steaming glazed ham. He held it up for Roberts to feast his eyes upon. He smacked his lips encouragingly.

"How'd you like to dig into this for dinner?" Rutter teased.

It was a wonderful-looking ham. It seemed as if it would be possible to reach right into the page and cut off a slice of it and eat it.

"Fine," Roberts said. His eyes held the ham lovingly. "What have you got to go with it?"

Griffiths tried very hard to make the most of the short rations. Even so, it meant that soup, for example, was served

L

twice a day—as a filler—instead of once, as before; bacon was served seldom and sparingly; and the ship's company had to eat more and more tinned meats and less and less of the frozen-meat products from New Zealand and Australia with which the ship had been stocked in Hong Kong. Butter, tea, sugar, and milk were cut down considerably.

Griffiths congratulated himself on having brought with him a volume called *The Encyclopædia of Modern Cooking*. He consulted it religiously in an effort to give the men some relief from the real monotony of their diet. He learned from it, for example, how to make Scotch eggs, a dish not ordinarily served in the Royal Navy. These are hard-boiled eggs covered in sausage-meat and dipped in butter and fried. They made a particular hit with the ship's company. Every Sunday, also, as a morale-booster, he baked a cake for tea, usually a sponge-cake dotted throughout with dried currants.

Every so often he came up with some further little delicacy as a special surprise, such as mince-pies with puff pastry, for which he saved the suet from the beef served at other meals. He made his own mincemeat, incidentally, out of dried apples, currants, and raisins, suet, a drop of his own rum ration, and some lemon cordial which he borrowed from the ward-room.

It was not until some time in July that McCarthy discovered a hundred additional pounds of flour (which accounts for the fact that their careful original calculations were one bag of flour out by the end of the month) in four-pound packets which had been in canteen stores for more than a year. Time and the tropics had filled these packets of flour with weevils and maggots, but at this stage nothing could be wasted. Griffiths sieved the unwanted guests—all of them, he hoped—out of the tainted flour and mixed the result with the untainted. Staple food stocks were now becoming desperately low.

The rats that annoyed the men on the mess-deck were even more troublesome in the galley. At first they gnawed their way into Griffiths' wooden bread-locker and tore ravenously into the loaves stored there. Griffiths felt that it boiled down to a battle between himself and two particularly insistent rats, one of which, he believed, was easily two feet long from sharp nose to tip of snake-like tail. These two, he swore, were visitors in the bread-box every night. He set traps and snares, but his two special *bêtes noires* always seemed able to keep out of trouble. Eventually Griffiths asked McCarthy for some fine wire mesh, and with this made the eight feet by four feet by three feet bread-locker thoroughly ratproof. From then on he kept not only all his bread but also his other rat-attracting food in the locker.

During all these goings-on Kerans' most important consideration, he thought, was in the maintaining of the high morale of his men. During the hundred and one days he had French wireless no fewer than two hundred and sixty-five telegrams from members of the crew to their dear ones at home. Most said more or less the same thing in more or less the same words:

SAFE AND WELL. STILL IN YANGTSE. CANNOT RECEIVE OR SEND MAIL.

One day the No. 1 trader gave Kerans four bottles of beer as a sample of what he was able to supply. Kerans decided to raffle the four bottles off. "There was more fuss over the winners," Kerans said later, "than if they had been the lucky ones in the draw of an Irish Sweep."

A week later the first consignment of Chinese beer arrived—enough for one bottle for every man on the ship. This was the first beer most of the ship's company had tasted since April, and the men sipped it slowly, savouring its flavour as if it were some priceless liqueur. The No. 1 trader had demanded, and received, twelve shillings and sixpence a bottle for it! The Commander-in-Chief had sanctioned the purchase by wireless, and long afterwards the Far East Central Amenities Fund reimbursed the British Treasury for the money thus expended.

Late in June a period of wet and windy weather set in. As a result of this miserably damp time, Kerans was confined for three days to his cabin with a painful attack of fibrositis. For

the three days it is doubtful if he could have walked if he had
had to.

Frank made an entry in his diary:

A very sad blow. Captain is ill due to weather and dampness
of ship. Without him we are lost.

Chapter Twenty-nine

THE MEETING

On the morning of July the 5th Kerans, now fully recovered from his fibrositis, had Frank brought to his cabin.

"I'm going ashore for another meeting with Colonel Kang this afternoon," he announced. "Would you like to come along to take notes?" By now Kerans was more than satisfied with the morale value of his policy of taking a different petty officer or key rating ashore with him to each meeting. Each time on the return of the *Amethyst* delegation the men from the lower deck would cluster excitedly round the petty officer, pumping him with eager questions. This lent variety, at least, to a period of over-dull waiting; and each time, Kerans believed, the ship was knit together more closely as a team.

"I'd like that very much, sir!"

Frank was, in fact, delighted at having been chosen. He had stuck faithfully to an earlier resolve to keep a diary of everything that had happened since *Amethyst* poked her trim bow into the waters of the Yangtse, and this would give him a most welcome opportunity to enlarge his field of observation. In addition, he had watched the new captain through the critical eyes which had seen twenty-four years of Navy experience; and he had come to admire Kerans greatly. Now he would have a chance to watch him in action against the Communists round a discussion table.

It was raining again. The drops pelted down from the overcast sky, fat and heavy and full of tropical fury. Kerans and Frank were dressed for the weather in mackintoshes, and over their heads carried incongruously coloured varnished Chinese paper umbrellas, which, surprisingly, were most effectively waterproof and strong, despite their frail appearance.

As he was about to board the sampan Kerans saw that the female members of the crew were unprotected against the rain. He shook his head. "Gran is too old for this kind of weather," he decided. "Better get her an oilskin."

Somebody got the oilskin and gave it to the ancient crone, but as soon as she put it on Cheesi and Midnight joined together in a loud, indignant howl of protest.

Then, giving Kerans frozen looks, they retreated under an emergency canvas lean-to they had stretched over part of the sampan to protect them from the downpour while they were waiting beside the ship for the *Amethyst* shore party to start for the meeting. Kerans needed no interpreter to tell him that they had spontaneously decided to strike because of what they obviously considered to be an act of outrageous favouritism towards Gran.

Kerans sighed. "Women!" he said. Then he ordered: "All right. Get two more oilskins for the girls."

The oilskins were brought up from stores. As soon as they saw them Cheesi and Midnight, all smiles, popped out from behind the canvas shelter. They slipped into the stiff garments, chattering and laughing and making a triumphant occasion of it. Then they took the sampan in to shore.

The meeting this time was held neither in Chingkiang nor at Chiao Shan Island, but in a large stone house in the near-by village of Ma Chan Shaw. The *Amethyst* party—Kerans, Frank, and the ship's interpreter—ducked into the entrance hall of the house, glad to be out of the rain, and immediately a Chinese Communist private soldier gave each the customary hot, dry towel, on which they wiped their streaming faces and wet hands. Then they sat down at a long table facing Kang and his interpreters.

"The atmosphere," Frank told Freeman later, "was very tense. There was something about it that made me feel excited."

Almost as soon as they arrived at the meeting the woman Press and Propaganda photographer pointed her Leica at Frank, a fresh victim for her persistent lens, and kept clicking away with it.

After the pouring of tea and the sipping of it for a prolonged moment Kang began abruptly to speak in Chinese. He was, Frank saw, about fifty years old and solidly built. He carried himself with a kind of grim arrogance. His interpreter translated as he spoke.

"I would like to stress again," Kang said (according to Captain Jen), "the points we brought out particularly at the meetings held on the 20th and 23rd of June. If the British side will acknowledge that they invaded Chinese waters without the authority of the Chinese People's Liberation Army an early solution to the proceeding of H.M.S. *Amethyst* down the river may be found. Talks on the question of your guilt and such other matters could then continue after *Amethyst* has gone."

Frank, busily scratching every word down on paper, thought, "He's going to let us go!" He was surprised when Kerans shook his head in stiff negation.

"The word 'invaded' is not to be used," Kerans said. "That is an assumption before it has been proven. Furthermore, it is a most serious word to use. Most serious indeed."

Kang tapped impatiently with his fingers on the table-top, but his expression did not vary.

"There may be some difference between the Chinese wording and the English wording. I don't know about that; but I have to abide by the Chinese wording."

A soldier brought a fresh pot of tea to the table, and poured some into each cup, filling them near to the brim. Kerans sipped at his.

"The word 'invade,'" he insisted, chewing on it like a dog on a bone, "means to commit a hostile act, which we certainly never intended to do, since, as you know, we are neutral. You cannot use the word 'invade.' That implies we had entered the Yangtse with intent to invade China—one small frigate— which is ridiculous."

"So this is what they mean by diplomacy," Frank thought. He wasn't sure he understood all the hidden currents, but he felt proud of Kerans and the way he was dealing with Kang.

The Chinese Colonel said, "Does Admiral Brind admit the British ships were guilty of entering the river?"

Kerans side-stepped the question, realizing that it would be a waste of time explaining to Kang that he could not speak for the Commander-in-Chief. "*I* recognize that *Amethyst* entered the Chinese national river and the Chinese People's Liberation Army frontier-zone without the especial permission of the Chinese People's Liberation Army." Kerans was trying very hard not to antagonize Kang, and he was taking great pains to express himself carefully and formally. He knew very well that by the time his words had passed through the phrasings of the interpreter they would sound even more stilted.

Kang's face was still cast in its dour mould. "The reason I have to use the word 'invade' is because *Amethyst* invaded Chinese sovereignty, and the matter of sovereignty is the principal consideration. If we study the use of the word in its full context it may help to bring our views together."

"You cannot use that word." Kerans was having a hard time trying to control his temper, and his voice was beginning to rise. It was always the same at each meeting: it seemed at first as if the two sides might achieve some kind of agreement, but in the end nothing was achieved except a maddening circular discussion which ended at the beginning, and with no decisions made or even any slight hope of a compromise. Kerans added, "It means that we are at war, and we are not. We are a friendly nation, and always have been."

Kang sipped at his tea, and set the cup down on the table carefully. He sucked his breath in between his gleaming teeth. "I suggest we leave this until a later meeting," he said stolidly.

Kerans' face lost its colour. This was a dismissal, an insult. "I insist," he said, "that the discussion continue." There was no mistaking the determination in his tone.

Kang said, "Very well. If Admiral Brind can admit the guilt of the British we can discuss the subject of compensation after *Amethyst* has gone."

Somewhere along the line Frank had lost the real thread of

the discussion. Most of it meant little to him; the parts that had real significance, he thought, were Kang's repeated references to *Amethyst's* departure. The last words the Communist Colonel said to Kerans on parting sang in Frank's ears: "I wish you good luck on the journey down-river."

Frank was elated. He thought, "Maybe I'll be seeing Kathleen and the kids again, after all." Like Williams earlier, he returned to the ship convinced that at long last *Amethyst* would be going down-river with a safe-passage very soon. The word saturated through the ship's company. The men slapped one another on the back; they even joked about their long, hot stay on the Yangtse under the tropic sun, joked about it as if it were all over.

Three days later Kerans went ashore to meet Kang again. Somehow *Amethyst's* men had decided that this one was to be the finally decisive meeting; this was to be the one when the Communists would agree to the safe-passage. Long before Kerans was due back the crew grouped on the quarterdeck waiting for his return and for the good news they fully expected to hear. Hawkins, Winfield, and Ormrod whispered together, a tight and tiny clique. There was Hartness, Garfitt, and Eric Saunders, and Griffiths and Logan and Connor, and other little groupings, all waiting and wondering and, now and then, breaking into nervous, edgy giggles.

"There he comes!"

The sampan had pushed off from the south shore, and presently it came alongside the ship.

"The captain's got a long face," Garfitt said uncertainly.

It was true: Kerans' face was long and unhappy and dark. The men waited, not wanting to release their hopeful optimism.

Kerans did not keep them long in doubt. He stepped aboard. "Sorry," he said. "Everything is off. I don't know now how long we'll be." He was feeling terribly depressed; his responsibility for the safety and well-being of the ship's company weighed heavily on him. He knew that if the safe-conduct were not very soon forthcoming there was only one extremely dangerous alternative solution for their plight, and he did not like to linger on thoughts of the casualties that seemed certain to come if it had to be tried.

All along Kerans had been making insistent demands of the Communists for additional oil-fuel. The men, he complained, were suffering from the intense heat—since he could not run the ventilators—and hadn't Colonel Kang made a constant point of his claim that he and the Chinese Communists had no quarrel with the British sailors themselves? Hadn't he repeatedly said that if there was anything he could do to make their life aboard the captive frigate more comfortable they had only to ask? Well, now he was asking, Kerans told him. Even his powder magazine, Kerans added, was in danger of blowing up if it were not kept cool—and how could he keep it cool without oil-fuel so that the ventilators could be run? Even the food would go bad if the refrigerators had to be shut off for still longer periods.

He kept hammering away at this need for fuel, without much hope that he would ever get it. And then, suddenly, it came—two hundred and ninety-six drums of it, containing fifty-four tons.

It came by junk from Nanking, and it was Admiralty fuel—though the Communists charged more than £400 for its delivery—and it had been saved up for a possible emergency in the months before the Communist troops had reached the Yangtse. Each ship arriving at Nanking had left behind a few drums of fuel, as many as she could spare. And now this Navy foresight had paid.

The drums were loaded on to *Amethyst* by hand-pulley, and the men rolled each barrel round to one of the three intakes which led to the ship's tanks, and emptied it, and then threw the empty on to the quarterdeck. From there each empty was tossed back aboard the junk down below.

Every one, officers and men, buckled down to the job of carrying the drums and emptying them into the intakes and throwing the empties back. Every one got blacker and greasier as the day wore on. Soon the decks were slippery with oil.

Griffiths and George Cavill were kept busy in the galley getting food for the hot and sweating men and keeping them supplied with iced lime-juice. Finally, at four o'clock in the afternoon of July the 10th, eleven hours after "Operation Oil" had begun, the last drum was emptied into *Amethyst's* tanks.

Every man on board was exhausted, but it was a sweet kind of exhaustion. The arrival of the oil had given the ship's company a much-needed boost of morale just when it had been about to sink to its lowest point since the original shelling. Now, the men knew, with new reserves of fuel, they would not have to suffer for such interminably long stretches without power and without ventilation.

With it all Kerans could not help but feel puzzled.

"I never will know," he remarked wonderingly to Hett, "why the Communists let us have it."

During all the meetings with the Communists Colonel Kang had spoken only in Chinese. He had waited patiently, almost blankly, for his interpreters to translate Kerans' words into his own language.

Then, at a meeting late in July, Kerans departed from his usual custom of taking a petty officer ashore with him, and took Strain instead. Kerans had been trying, without succeeding in arousing any interest, to convince Kang that *Amethyst* should have another shipment of fuel: the fifty-six tons would not last very long, he explained; they would soon be as badly off as ever. Towards this end he had been outlining the difficulties further power-cuts would raise on the ship.

The meeting broke up, as usual, with nothing apparent having been accomplished. Just as he was about to leave Kerans saw, to his utter amazement, Kang motion Strain aside, and heard him ask, in perfectly good English, "Are conditions on board really as bad as Kerans says? Is the heat as bad as he says it is?"

Strain, of course, said that Kerans had not been exaggerating. The *Amethyst* men left for their ship.

In the sampan Strain said, "I thought you told me that this chap Kang couldn't speak any English?"

"That's right," Kerans grinned ruefully, "I did. It only goes to show that you can't trust anybody these days, doesn't it?"

Chapter Thirty

GLORIA

As early as mid-May Kerans reserved a corner of his mind for thinking about a possible break-out from the river in case his negotiations for a safe-conduct should fail. With this in mind he decided to get the ship into seaworthy shape as soon as possible. He appointed Garns and Saunders, under the supervision of Strain, as a damage-control party, which soon became jocularly known among the ship's company as the Wrecker's Union. But Kerans did not mention to anyone his secret fears that a break-out might eventually become the only avenue to freedom.

Garns and Saunders pitched in with great enthusiasm. They busily stuffed hammocks with mattresses and blankets and old clothing—anything they could lay their hands on that could be spared. Then they took these bulging, sausage-like wads and stuffed them into the gaping shell-holes. They used from one to three of these at a time, according to the size of the hole.

After that they shored up the damaged area with planks, using the stock of timber—which they cut down to the proper sizes—which, fortunately, had been taken aboard in Malaya some time previously. In a month they had succeeded in adequately filling in eight holes along the waterline; but one waterline hole, dead astern and directly over the rudder, resisted all their efforts. During this time Garns' official period of service in the Navy came to a close.

Garns was a short, sandy-haired man of about thirty years of age. "Here I am, stuck," he said sadly to Saunders. He had been in the Navy for twelve years. "One thing I can tell you, though: the Navy will never get me again after this. No, sir!"

Saunders grinned.

"Don't be an ass, Garnsey. Don't you know you'll never get out of this predicament? Don't you know you'll never be demobbed now?"

Garns gave him a long, sideways look of suspicion. "*You'll* be soldiering on, me lad," he said, "long after *I* get back to Civvy Street. And, brother, am I going to have the laugh on you!"[1]

Kerans did his utmost, during this trying period of negotiating and waiting for the safe-conduct and of getting nowhere with the Communists, to keep his men occupied. He knew that he had no enemies worse than idleness and boredom and dropping morale. He kept the ship to a strict Service routine—regular times of duty, regular jobs to do. He appointed Rees as schoolmaster, so that the boy-seamen and junior ratings could continue with their studies and not sacrifice their chances of promotion because of *Amethyst's* captivity.

On the night of July the 1st the ship was very nearly rammed by a Chinese ship which was going down-river. Kerans thought, "If the Chinese can navigate the Yangtse at night, why can't I?"

It was, he decided, an idea well worth considering from all angles. Artillery-fire was less likely to be accurate by night. The element of surprise was an important factor after dark. In his mind *Amethyst's* captain was formulating the first vague outlines of a workable escape plan.

Kerans still said nothing about the possibility of a break-out to either officers or men. Instead, when he ordered large chunks of the frigate's superstructure to be cut away—to alter the ship's silhouette and to reduce top-weight for greater stability—he explained it, even to Hett, Strain, and Fearnley, as a further move in his campaign to maintain morale by keeping his men busy. He trusted his crew completely; but security was a matter of life or death.

"Suppose the Chinese on board should get wind of the fact

[1] For the record, it is interesting to note that Garns has signed up since for another term of service in the Navy.

that I'm contemplating a break-out?" he thought. "Suppose one of them, even unintentionally, should let something slip to the sampan girls or the traders?"

Even the most slender risk was far too great to take.

Kerans was greatly handicapped by the fact that the secret code-books had been destroyed on April the 20th, when it was thought that *Amethyst* was about to be abandoned. He could not, because of that, advise Admiral Brind in plain language over the wireless of his plans for a dash to safety. The Communists, he knew, were monitoring the air, and they would surely pick up the message themselves and take firm precautions to prevent the escape. Nevertheless, on July the 7th, he did signal the Commander-in-Chief:

WOULD BE GRATEFUL YOUR ADVICE PLEASE ON MY ACTIONS IF MENACED BY TYPHOON.

Kerans knew that typhoons were not at all unusual along the Yangtse. He also knew that this query, a ridiculously elemental one which an officer in His Majesty's Navy would never need to ask, would not be taken at its face-value in Hong Kong. He was simply asking in veiled terms for permission to break out if the opportunity offered itself.

Brind replied at once.

TYPHOONS UNLIKELY REACH YOU IN SERIOUS STRENGTH AND YOU ARE IN GOOD HOLDING GROUND. THE GOLDEN RULE OF MAKING AN OFFING AND TAKING PLENTY OF SEA-ROOM APPLIES PARTICULARLY.

Kerans read the Admiral's message through again and again. "The golden rule of making an offing and taking plenty of sea-room applies particularly." He was reasonably convinced that this meant that he had been given permission to run for it if he chose; but he could not be certain. The first part of the message seemed to contradict the second. The difficulty, of course, was that any double meaning subtle enough to escape the attention of the Communists would always leave some room for doubt. The sending of any completely clear-cut message was virtually impossible.

On the 24th of July *Amethyst* met Gloria. Gloria was, in fact, a typhoon, thus named by the Americans, who not only kept a careful tab on the course of such violent storms, but also named each of them by a different female Christian name.

Knowing that typhoons were prevalent in the area, Kerans had long since made a mental note to the effect that there was a possibility of escaping down the river during the blinding, torrential rain just before or just after the passing of one of these tropical storms; but, although he had been informed by wireless that Gloria was on her way, he had been given insufficient details about her strength, and did not know, for example, how close her centre would come to the ship's anchorage.

As it happened, the centre of the storm passed very close to the frigate. To make use of Gloria as escape cover Kerans would have had to raise steam several hours in advance, and, perhaps, use much of his remaining fuel to no purpose. Even after the fifty-six-ton shipment of oil from Nanking there was now none to spare.

With this in mind, and because of the shortage of vital information about the storm, Kerans decided after much consideration that it was too risky to chance using the typhoon for a break-out attempt. It might easily result in the wrecking of *Amethyst*. He crossed it off the list of escape possibilities.

During the time Gloria raged great masses of earth dropped from the Yangtse's muddy banks into the current. River traffic, of course, had long since scurried to safe anchorage. No boats moved on the river. Melting snows from the faraway Himalaya Mountains had poured thousands of miles down the Yangtse's channel, adding to the flooding. By now the water was several feet above normal level. The current was roaring madly downstream.

Frank, standing at the rail, saw a dog sitting comfortably, if a little sadly, on a haystack as it floated down on the moving stream of flood-water. Later he saw a chicken perched on top

A Message that was never sent

Message giving the Command to Kerans

*Ripped by Shell Fragments, the White Ensign
flying after the Action*
Photo Planet News

of its floating pen. After a while a house roared down on the quickening current. Then several pigs went by, struggling with no effect against the raging current. Some of the stokers decided to try to rescue one of the pigs as it swept by.

"It'll make a nice change in diet," one of the stokers said.

He tied a rope to a duckboard—a grilled board, four feet square—and threw the board over the side as a kind of raft. The pig saw the wooden grill floating near him on the water and tried to swim over to it and scramble aboard; but the current of the Yangtse was now far too wild for a mere pig to conquer. It swept on, struggling more feebly every minute.

Frank deduced, correctly, that large areas of low-lying land along the Yangtse must now be under water. He wondered how long it would be before the current stopped accelerating. He thought, "Kang says he'll blast us out of the river if we move. What happens if the anchor parts?" He couldn't get rid of the clammy hand of fear.

At just about this time, by a coincidence, French was sending a message to Hong Kong from Kerans. It read:

IF CABLE PARTS WILL RUN FOR IT AND IF WRECKED AND SALVAGE IMPOSSIBLE WILL BLOW UP SHIP.

M

Chapter Thirty-one

"ICHABOD!"

Gloria went her wayward way, leaving *Amethyst* still anchored solidly, and with the Yangtse high and angry and roiled and speeding faster than ever towards the open sea; a hundred and fifty miles distant.

By now Kerans knew that if he was going to break out for freedom without waiting for the safe-passage, which in all likelihood would never be granted, he was going to have to do it soon. Very soon!

The supply of oil on board was sinking again, and it could not go down much farther and still leave him enough to get out of the river. The question was how could he, without giving his intention away to the vigilant Communists, let the Commander-in-Chief know of his plan?

He tried to think of a way.

Sitting alone in his small cabin, he ran over his past experience, searching in the nooks and crannies of his memory, hoping that a scheme would somehow present itself. He had almost given up, and his thoughts had wandered homeward, as they often did, to his pretty blonde wife and his fair-haired small daughter when, suddenly, he sat up straight and snapped his fingers.

"Got it!" he said.

He had remembered that in his earlier days, when he was newly married, he and his wife, Stephanie, had concocted a code, so that he could at times, and harmlessly, pass a message to her. It was the sort of private code nearly all members of the armed forces overseas used with their families during the War. In this private code of the Kerans' the word 'Ichabod' had come to mean 'I'm coming home.'

Kerans had French tap out a personal message to Mrs Kerans:

HAVE YOU RECEIVED TEN POUNDS FROM THE BANK? WRITE AND TELL GOLDSMITHS I CAN'T PAY AS STILL IN COMMUNIST HANDS. ICHABOD. KERANS.

The operative word, of course, was 'Ichabod'—'I'm coming home.' The remainder of the message was pure invention. Kerans knew that this message would be passed through Naval Headquarters in Hong Kong, and then through the Admiralty in London, before it reached his wife. He hoped some inquisitive naval man would wonder about the meaning of 'Ichabod,' and would check with Stephanie about it. Even if this failed he felt reasonably sure that, realizing the significance of the code message, she would inform the Admiralty about it.

In due course Hong Kong passed the telegram on to the Admiralty, and the Admiralty passed it on to Mrs Kerans, who was at the time living in Littlehampton. She read it, completely puzzled, and becoming more and more worried as she thought about it. It had been a long time since she and Kerans had used their code, long enough for her to have forgotten it completely. She already had plenty to worry about. Now she had something else.

"I wonder what's the matter with John?" she tortured herself. "It isn't like him not to make sense." 'Ichabod' no longer meant anything to her.

Chapter Thirty-two

DECISION

A day or two after the passing of the typhoon Kerans issued what seemed to be an extraordinary order.

"I want the cable lashed with bedding," he said. "But first I want the bedding to be soaked thoroughly in soft soap and grease."

There were blank faces around him.

"Every time the ship swings at her moorings," Kerans added by way of explanation, "the cable screeches and scrapes. It's getting on my nerves."

This was not his true reason for giving the order, but he left it at that. He was still taking no chances that his secret might get out; but he had been making plans for the break-out that covered the smallest eventuality.

"The vital point in breaking out," he thought, "will be in slipping the cable and turning the ship without making a noise. The whole getaway will hinge on that. One sudden sound, and we'll be blown right out of the water."

Kerans had very recently received word, through a channel that cannot, even now, be revealed, that if he made the decision to try a break-out he would have the full approval of the Commander-in-Chief, Far East Station; and, by the same still-secret source, he had been informed that he had political clearance from London.

He had known for some time now that he would have to make up his mind one way or another very soon. His calculations showed that at least thirty tons of usable fuel would be needed to carry him down the river to the open sea at full power, and that seventeen tons would be lost in suction. At least forty-seven tons would be needed in the tanks, then, if the ship was to get out of the Yangtse.

On the morning of July the 30th Williams reported to him that only fifty-three tons were left in the tanks. This left him with the jarring realization that if he delayed his decision for more than a few days he would have no decision to make: he would be unable to leave the river because he simply would not have the oil to run his engines. He knew, too, that while all on board (thanks to Fearnley's preventative care) were at the moment physically fit, that situation would not last for ever. Food was getting to be in dangerously short supply. Officers and men had subsisted on half-rations for two weeks now, and these would very shortly have to be cut drastically once again. Flour was almost exhausted; the remaining yeast and sugar had gone bad; and because of the flooding of the farmlands along the banks of the river it was very likely that fresh foods would soon become unavailable from shore.

In addition, he had just heard over the ship's radio on the B.B.C. news that the only other British ship trapped in the Yangtse, *Anchises*, a Blue Funnel liner, which had been bombed by the Nationalists in June, had, with Communist permission, sailed down the river to safety. It had not been a major factor in his calculations, but he had worried previously that if *Amethyst* had made a run for it the Communists might have kept *Anchises* in retaliation.

Kerans piled up his arguments in favour of a break-out. There was, of course, the element of surprise. After all these months of sitting quietly at anchor would the guarding guns on shore expect an attempted escape?

Important too was the fact that Kerans had reason to believe that Colonel Kang, his No. 1 watchdog, was at the moment paying a duty visit to headquarters in Nanking. Gloria and the melting snows from Tibet had carried the level of the Yangtse up over some of the original battery positions, and Kerans hoped that these were in the process of being resited on high ground. He had seen large gangs of soldiers working on the roads, many of which had been flooded. All this would create unusual communications difficulties for the Communists.

Then, again, although Williams and his engineroom men had put the machinery into tip-top operational condition, Kerans was aware that *Amethyst's* evaporator was on its last legs. Without it there would be no drinking-water aboard the ship.

Then there was the important question of morale: it was reasonably high now, but with the still-rising heat and the worsening conditions that time would inevitably bring it could not be maintained for ever. Even medical supplies were running low, and Fearnley had long since ceased to treat any of the local Chinese. Disinfectant, which was of vital importance in the tropics, was dwindling away, and even the shortage of latrine paper had become an acute problem.

At three o'clock on the afternoon of the 30th of July Kerans said to himself, "It's got to be now or never." When he made the decision he was sitting on a steel bollard in the sun. He sent for Strain.

"George," he said, "look, old boy, I'm going to break out to-night."

Chapter Thirty-three

BREAK-OUT

The electrical officer was stunned. The ship had rested there, tied to the muddy bottom, for a hundred days. Strain stared at Kerans, unable to believe the evidence of his ears.

"I'll give you my reasons," Kerans said.

The hot sun was beating down upon them. There was the sleepy buzzing of flies and the murmur of voices from different parts of the ship. It was very peaceful, and the thought of a naval action seemed distant and unreal. Kerans continued, outlining his problems and explaining how he came to his decision. He spoke quietly and seriously, just above a whisper.

"To-night will be the last one for another month with the phase of the moon just right for a break-out," he said. "The moon is due to set at eleven o'clock. I've decided to slip away at ten, accepting one hour of the waning moon as an unavoidable handicap. We'll need every minute of time if we hope to get past the big guns at Woosung before dawn." He paused.

"The Yangtse is still very high, as you can see, because of Gloria," he went on, "but it's due to fall very soon. And, travelling by night without a river pilot, we'll need all the water we can to take us over the mud-banks. Besides, food is getting short, and we probably won't get much in the way of fresh vegetables from now on." Kerans waved towards the flooded shores.

"It adds up," Strain said. He was calmer now.

"Then," Kerans said, "there is the element of surprise after all the months of standing still." He paused and looked straight into Strain's eyes. "Those are my reasons for wanting to break out. I've been thinking about them a great deal. Now I want you to give me any reasons why we should not."

Strain began to look pleased. The idea was sinking in, and it felt good. "I can't think of any," he said. His face broke into a slow smile.

Shortly before six o'clock Kerans said to Hett, "Look, go get the charts and prepare them in the right order. We're going to break out to-night."

The young officer's face lit up, making him look even more schoolboyish than usual. He ran off like a rabbit after the charts.

Kerans was feeling pretty good about the break-out now that the decision had been made. He had worked out all the angles, quietly and alone, during the long, tiresome wait. He knew that the ship might *not* reach safety, but it was to-night or never. Logic told him that there was no choice.

He drew up a list of seventeen petty officers and key ratings, and ordered them to meet in his cabin at about eight that evening. By now Strain, Hett, Fearnley, and Engineroom Artificer Williams knew of the impending break-out. The rest of the ship's company went about their duties all unsuspecting.

The seventeen trooped silently into Kerans' small cabin. There was not much room to spare. The door was shut, and almost at once the air became stifling.

"I'm going to break out to-night at ten," Kerans said matter-of-factly.

Somebody let out a low whistle.

There was not much light in the cabin, but enough to reveal a pattern of pale, tense faces. Somebody coughed.

"As far as the engineroom personnel are concerned," Kerans said, "I want everything they can give me. And I mean everything. I'll not give the order for full ahead except in a real emergency. If we come under fire I shall ask for smoke. Understand?"

One or two of the men nodded silently. Some of them were still stunned. Garns, who had been put in charge of the quarterdeck—ordinarily a petty officer's job—suddenly felt sick in his stomach.

"As for those on the guns," Kerans continued, "fire will not be opened until we have been fired on."

Somebody cleared his throat.

"You, French!" Kerans said.

"Yes, sir?"

"W.T. silence will be enforced until I am ready to send a message. Then only flash procedure will be used." This meant that each message would be preceded by the single word 'flash.' The signal that followed would then get top priority from every ship and from every other receiver anywhere in the world.

"Yes, sir," French said. His voice sounded thin in the crowded room.

"Now, then," Kerans said crisply, but not liking this part of it, "if we are hit and sinking I will beach the ship, if possible, to save lives. The ship's company will get ashore. Then I will blow up *Amethyst*. I will make the last signal myself before destroying the W.T. office. If disaster does come your main object is to reach Shanghai or escape in junks to the open sea."

It was hot. Kerans wiped his brow with a handkerchief. "Pass the information along to the ship's company," he said, "but watch the Chinese. We don't want to give the show away now. Good luck to you all. I hope we make it. At least, we'll have a damn good shot at it."

McNamara, the canteen manager, was standing at the rail, thinking of his home in Upper Norwood and of how much cooler it would be there. He saw Frank step out on deck, and was surprised at the tension he saw in his dark face.

"What's happening, Frankie?" McNamara asked. "What's the buzz?"

"We're going for a little trip," Frank said. His voice was very calm—too calm.

McNamara felt a flutter in his stomach. "What do you mean, a little trip?"

"Why, Damager, I mean we're going to try to make a run for it."

McNamara's grin was twisted. "Don't be so bloody silly, Les."

"We are. The captain intends to make a dash for it to-night."

"*To-night?*" McNamara refused at first to believe that it was true. A moment later he saw Williams collecting his stokers quietly together, and he watched them file down the stoke-hole into the boiler-house.

"By God, it's true!" he thought. "It's really true!"

Somebody tapped his elbow. "Lieutenant Hett wants to see you, Damager. He's in the charthouse."

McNamara reported to Hett. Hett said, "McNamara, what do you know about charts?"

"Nothing, sir."

"Well, now's your chance to learn." He showed McNamara a set of about a dozen charts which followed one another down the Yangtse as far as Woosung, the fortress near the mouth of the river. The first chart, which covered the area in which *Amethyst* had for so long rested at anchor, was torn and blood-stained from the first action. The blood on it belonged to Berger, who had been evacuated on that distant April day.

Hett showed McNamara the course down-river as it had been marked on the charts by Kerans.

"I want you to stay inside the charthouse," Hett told him, "and follow the course all the way down. If the bridge is hit and destroyed you will still know the course, and the ship can carry on. I'll call out the different landmarks to you over the voice-pipe as we come to them. All right?"

"Yes, sir," McNamara said. He could feel a nerve jumping near the base of his jaw. "I'm scared," he thought. "I'm really scared." He tried not to remember what it had been like during the first action.

He thumbed through the charts for a while, familiarizing himself with them. Then he went below to his canteen and collected cigarettes to distribute to the ship's company. They would need them, and he knew he would have no time to pass them round later.

Winfield had been sitting on the quarterdeck, reading a dog-eared copy of *Picturegoer* by the fading light, when Petty Officer William Venton came over and threw a hand on to his shoulder.

"Grease the sirens, Ken," Venton said. "We're leaving. Grease them so the brass won't shine."

"You're kidding, Joe!"

"I'm not kidding, Ken." Venton told him about Kerans' decision. Winfield too felt a brief, panicky fluttering in his stomach. Then, after a while, when the dusk had deepened a little, he climbed up to the sirens on the funnel ladder and greased them heavily.

He felt curiously detached from reality. "All this is happening to some one else," he thought. They had been cooped up in the river for so long that any other kind of life seemed like a dream which could not possibly come true.

The ship was almost set for the getaway.

B-gun's magazines were loaded and ready. Black paint had been thrown over the white surfaces of the superstructure. The watertight doors were shut. Great sheets of canvas had hurriedly been stretched along the sides of the frigate to transform her silhouette as much as possible. The machinery was oiled up. A head of steam had already been raised earlier in order to generate power for transmitting wireless signals.

Winfield said to Williams, "I wonder what old Colonel Kang will say to-morrow when he's dipped to a private?"

Williams chuckled as he thought of Kang's embarrassment. "I wonder?" he said.

McCarthy had ordered potatoes and eggs and cabbages and beer from the traders that morning. He had told them to have the supplies on board by seven in the evening, and they had not come. Still, he was not worried about it. They were often a day late in arriving, and by to-morrow who would care?

Now he was very busy and had no time to think of the traders. He had supplied Griffiths with enough bread for sandwiches and with cocoa and tea for the trip down. He was getting first-aid kits ready in case they were needed. He hoped that they wouldn't be needed.

Somebody shouted down to him in a frightened voice. "Stores P.O.! Stores P.O.! Your traders are coming out!"

"My God," McCarthy thought wildly, "not now!" He rushed up on to the deck. The sampan was nearing the ship.

Kerans was there. Kerans was everywhere. He spoke calmly and crisply, as if there were no danger, as if there was no risk that the traders might report the ship's preparations to the Communists on shore.

"You'll have to do without an interpreter," Kerans said. "He might say something to tip them off. Don't let them go past the top of the gangway; and get rid of them as quickly as possible."

Kerans turned to the men gathered on the deck.

"Bring camp-beds to the quarterdeck right away," he ordered, "and temporarily stop the preparations for the break-out. Some of you men undress and turn in on the camp-beds. Make it look good." He left McCarthy to deal with the traders.

McCarthy stood at the gangway, blocking it.

"Hello," he said as the traders came alongside. They grinned and passed the potatoes, eggs, cabbages, and beer up from the sampan.

The No. 1 trader handed an invoice to McCarthy. He checked it. "Hey!" he said, trying to keep a tremor out of his voice. "You're five hundred cattis of potatoes short."

The No. 1 trader nodded.

"I pay you to-morrow when you bring rest," McCarthy said. The trader seemed to understand.

"In morning," the trader said. "In morning."

"That's right." McCarthy smiled, trying to keep all signs of nervousness away from his face. "In the morning."

The sampan pushed off. McCarthy let out a long, relieved breath. He was pretty sure that he had got away with it, and that the traders had noticed nothing out of the way. There was murmuring of voices behind him on the ship. Then he realized that for the past several minutes there had been nothing but expectant silence around him.

With darkness they cleared the camp-beds away from the quarterdeck. They made as little noise as possible. Kerans, who had spent long nights observing the flow of civilian traffic up and down the Yangtse, ordered Communist river-lights rigged.

"A green light over a red is the ticket for travelling downstream," he said.

He tried to eat a cold meal, but was unable to get it down. He ordered steel helmets to be issued to the men who would be stationed on the upper deck. Then, at nine o'clock, he climbed up on to the bridge to accustom his eyes to the darkness. At ten o'clock all was ready.

Kerans waited for a few minutes for the moon to disappear behind some friendly clouds. The moon, fortunately, was on the south side of the river. It would not silhouette the ship for the Communist battery.

He thought he heard a motor pulsing somewhere. He listened intently. Then all at once he saw her—a merchant ship rounding Ta-sha Island on her way down-river.

He thought: "Just what the doctor ordered! Something I can follow!"

He waited until the ship passed *Amethyst's* anchorage. Then, at seven minutes past ten o'clock, he ordered, "Obey telegraphs!"

The first movement of the main engines came at nine minutes past ten. Kerans ordered the port engine half ahead.

"Slip cable!" he said.

Amethyst was anchored with her bow facing upstream. Kerans heard the pin being knocked out of the cable-join, and waited, wondering anxiously if the cable, wrapped even as it was in greased cloth, would make a noise and give them away.

He heard no splash, no splash at all.

"Starboard engine half astern!" he ordered. The port engine was still at half ahead. Using full wheel, and helped by the galloping current, *Amethyst* made a full turn in less than a minute.

Just as the turn was completed Kerans looked up. He saw a gushing shower of sparks leave the funnel, caused by the shaky brickwork in one of the boilers. He held his breath and remained motionless. He waited for the Communist gunfire.

None came.

Under his breath Kerans said, "Whew!" He was perspiring freely.

Now *Amethyst* was headed in the right direction. The race for freedom had at last begun.

They waited, down in the engineroom, for the word to start the engines. They waited silently, sweating already, and eager to get it over with, since it had to be done. Williams kept thinking of what had happened on the way up-river. "If we can just get past Rose Island," he thought, the memory of things past unreasonably stuck in his mind, "we'll be all right."

Word came down from the bridge to start the port engine. The ship was alive again for the first time since April.

"It was a fine feeling," Winfield said later. "It's like being in a graveyard to be in a dead ship."

Winfield was on the voice-pipe taking orders direct from the bridge. When the order came down for half ahead on both engines he knew that they had turned completely and were on the way down.

They had not been hit. They had made the turn. The men in the engineroom exchanged pleased glances. Williams held his thumbs up and grinned.

The first great danger was past.

They had been following close on the heels of the merchant ship, the *Kiang Ling Liberation*, for a quarter of an hour when a flare tore away the darkness ahead of them. The flare, obviously meant for the ship ahead, had been shot up from the Communist battery at Tachiang. The *Kiang Ling Liberation* replied to the flare by sounding her siren anxiously. In the flood of light Kerans noticed a small naval patrol vessel not far off his port bow.

"This is it," he thought.

A second silvery flare shot up, this time intended for *Amethyst*. Kerans made no attempt to reply, but continued on his way.

The rattle of small-arms fire burst into the night. To Kerans' complete bewilderment and pleasure the Communist patrol-boat suddenly opened fire with Oerlikon tracer on the Communist shore batteries. He could only assume that the captain of the patrol-boat had completely lost his head in the sudden chaos. Then *Amethyst* came under heavy artillery and small-arms fire from the shore. The shells sang overhead and fell around her.

"Full ahead both!" Kerans ordered. Almost as he spoke the ship heeled over about thirty-five degrees to starboard.

"The engineroom's been hit badly," Kerans thought despairingly. He was sure he could hear the water gushing in.

"Open fire!" he shouted. "And keep on firing until the end!"

Because of the extreme list B-gun could not immediately be brought to bear. *Amethyst*'s Oerlikon and her four Bren guns stuttered and barked. Kerans looked around in the dying light of the second flare for a suitable place to beach the ship, a place which would take him out of the line of fire from the batteries. He yelled down the voice-pipe to Strain.

"Tell French to flash a message to Hong Kong." Then he dictated the message:

I AM UNDER HEAVY FIRE AND HAVE BEEN HIT.

He had barely finished speaking when, almost miraculously, the ship righted herself. Kerans has never been absolutely certain what it was that caused *Amethyst* to heel over so sharply. The ship had not, in fact, been hit after all; but very probably a large shell, exploding in the water very close to her, had created violent under-surface currents. Later some plates on the ship's waterline were discovered to have been newly sprung, which supported this theory.

Winfield, at the voice-pipe in the engineroom, heard the firing. Kerans' shout whistled down to him.

"Make smoke!"

A moment later Winfield heard a loud, only slightly muffled explosion that seemed to come from very near to where he stood. *Amethyst* shuddered. Black smoke poured down the fan-shafts into the engineroom, and Winfield looked around him wildly, thinking, "We're hit! We're hit!"

The faces of the men in the engineroom were tilted almost prayerfully towards the deck. They looked bloodless and blank with surprise. Somebody shouted down the hatchway: "It's all right, mates! It's our own gun." The faces looked down to their work again, wearing relieved little smiles.

"I'm planning the menu of what I'm going to order for my first meal at the Fleet Club in Hong Kong," Leading Stoker Duncan McDonald boomed with sudden, mock solemnity. "You know what it's going to be? Steak and eggs and chips—yes, sir!"

"Aw," Bannister said, "you're gettin' to sound just like Roberts, you are."

One or two of the men near by laughed nervously. Tension was still high.

By weaving like a ballet-dancer and by making black smoke *Amethyst* slipped past the *Kiang Ling Liberation*. The merchant-ship had turned sharply to port, and, in a frenzied attempt to be recognized, was blowing crazily on her sirens. But at the same time she had switched off all her lights.

Amethyst's B-gun managed to get one four-inch shell away —the explosion which Winfield mistakenly thought had travelled in the other direction—and, to Kerans' surprise, this caused a fire ashore. But as soon as *Amethyst* had gathered full headway again he ordered the gun to cease firing. He feared that the give-away flash with each shot would enable the

Communist gunners to get a fix on the ship. Most of the Bren and Oerlikon fire from shore was passing well over *Amethyst*; but the 75- and 105-millimetre guns were dropping their shells round her with such alarming accuracy that they did everything but hit the ship.

One large shell, in fact, whistled so close to the back of Kerans' neck that he turned instinctively, as if it were possible for him to catch sight of it whizzing by. He was surprised and for a moment slightly unnerved to note that the shell had cut through the wireless aerial within inches of his head. As he turned he also caught sight of flames up-river, licking away near the surface of the water and reflecting in mad, upside-down activity. The merchant-ship was now aground and fiercely ablaze. In spite of its sirens, the Communist gunners had made a target of the *Kiang Ling Liberation*.

In the brief maelstrom of firing a great deal of damage had been done, almost all of it on the Communists themselves and by their own gunfire. Taking advantage of all this, Kerans had slipped *Amethyst* neatly through and under and around the wild barrage.

However, one thing was now certain: the gaff was blown. *Amethyst's* getaway was no longer a hard-held secret.

Kerans could only just see both banks of the river in the dark. At its widest point and in spate the Yangtse was about a mile across; at its narrowest perhaps half that. The frigate slipped past Rose Island, where she had gone aground so long before, without incident.

Reports came up from the engineroom that *Amethyst* was flooding badly from the one waterline hole, right in the stern, which Garns and Saunders had been unable to repair. Pumps were put into action to keep the water in check. Kerans prayed: "Dear God, don't let it flood so badly that it will put paid to my steering."

Down in the engineroom Winfield was bathed in sweat. It poured out of his scalp and down his brow and into his eyes, making them smart with the salt. Near him a man fainted with the heat. The temperature close to the voice-pipe was 170°; in

N

the boiler-room 130°; on the manœuvring platform, 125°.
Winfield left the voice-pipe while a mate took over; he rushed
up to the galley. He got a can of tea from Griffiths and took it
down to his mates in their sweating, steaming hell. There were
only eleven men in the engineroom, fewer than half the normal
complement, but before that night was over they would have
drunk ten gallons of tea. The moisture ran out of their pores
in never-ending rivulets, and they had to get it back into their
bodies somehow; so they drank tea.

In the sick bay, long since put in order, Fearnley waited with
Howell for the casualties to come in. Afterwards Fearnley
said, "I was scared stiff. There was nothing to do but sit and
wait."

In the chartroom McNamara followed the course. Beside
him, sharing the small room, James Bryson and Jack Day took
turns at calling up the depths as they appeared on the echo-
sounder. "Six fathoms . . . six and a half fathoms . . . seven
fathoms . . ." There was not much light in the corner of the
room near the echo-sounder, and they held up candles to get
their readings.

Shortly before one o'clock in the morning *Amethyst*, still
pushing ahead at full speed, approached Kiang Yin, the river-
port at which she had stopped for the night on her way up, a
hundred and one days before. The Communists had, of course,
long since crossed the river. Now they lay in wait there
behind their guns; but even the guns were not the great danger.

There was the boom.

All the way down, from the moment he had ordered the
slipping of the cable, Kerans had thought about the boom at
Kiang Yin. He had worried about it. He had turned it over
and over in his mind, examining his chances of getting through
it. Finally he had decided there was nothing he could do.

It was a gamble, pure and simple. The ship's continued life
or her sudden, bottom-ripping death depended on finding the
channel through the boom to safety, and he was not even sure
what kind of a boom it was.

Reports said that it was a line of sunken ships, just under the surface, placed across the river so that nothing could go up or down except through a narrow, heavily gun-guarded channel. All the way down the river, clenching and unclenching his fists, Kerans thought, "We've got to find that channel." He would have to risk the concentrated fire of the guns. There was always a chance, however slender, that *Amethyst* would escape serious damage even at point-blank range: she had done it once already on the trip down.

But if she ran headlong into the semi-sunken hulks only one thing was sure: she would slice off her bottom; she would peel it off like the skin of a ripe banana; she would let in the murky, gushing water of the Yangtse. And she would be finished.

Kiang Yin was just ahead.

Kerans strained on the bridge, listening for the first shell, throwing his eyes at the blank wall of darkness ahead. "Where is the damned boom?" He knew the ship was riding with Chance, beyond reason, beyond judgment. He knew that all he could do was drive on at full speed, waiting for the worst and hoping for the best.

A flare shot into the night. It echoed, silver-bright and falsely gay, in the broken surface of the water. As it did artillery thundered, and the river burst into a giant witch's cauldron of climbing waterspouts.

"Give me black smoke!" Kerans yelled down the voice-pipe. "Give me all the smoke you can make!"

The ship's bow was riding on a rail of white foam. She was travelling down the river at full speed, helped along by the five-knot current. Down below the engines whined and whirred. Williams and Winfield and Bannister and the rest concentrated grimly on their jobs, not thinking of the boom, not thinking that, at any moment, the bottom of the ship might be torn away on the sunken wrecks, and they with it.

Then, just ahead, Kerans saw a light.

"The boom!" he thought. But there was one light only, and

his chart had showed that there should be two, with the channel, thus marked, between them.

Near the light he could make out the grim, waiting silhouette of a patrol vessel. Thin, reaching lines of tracer fingered out from it erratically towards *Amethyst*. None of the bullets found their mark.

They were almost on the light, and Kerans had to make his gamble. Should he pass it to the right or to the left? There was no time to weigh the pros and cons, and there were no pros and cons to weigh.

Down the voice-pipe he spoke to Frank, at the wheel. "Steer just to port of the light," he said, making it sound crisp and decisive, as if there were no doubt about it at all. Then, silently, he prayed that he had guessed correctly.

The light was a hundred yards away.

Fifty!

Ten!

And he was through, clean through, without a scratch or a scrape. The ship was slicing full speed down the flooded Yangtse in the darkness of night towards the open sea. But there were still many miles of river to navigate. There were still many guns to pass.

Kerans began to shiver a little. For the first time he noticed that the night had become quite cool.

At about half-past two on the morning of July the 31st, with *Amethyst* still running at full speed on both engines, Day croaked up the voice-pipe to Kerans, "Echo-sounder reads only three fathoms of water, sir!" Both he and Saunders had become quite hoarse from yelling the depths constantly up the pipe.

Three fathoms of water left little margin for safety. *Amethyst's* normal salt-water draught was about nine feet, but now, with the Yangtse's fresh water coming in through the shell-hole in her stern, she was sitting lower than she should. Kerans ordered Frank to steer sharply to starboard into deeper water. Then, suddenly, he saw a patrol vessel loom up out of the darkness ahead. His heart sank. Was this another, totally unexpected control-point? Kerans decided that his only move was to get as close to the vessel as possible and try to smother her fire in *Amethyst's* superstructure.

He shouted new orders down to Frank, and the frigate scraped by the patrol vessel with a bare eighteen inches to spare. There were no casualties; there was no damage.

At eighteen minutes to three Kerans sent another message down for French to dispatch to Hong Kong:

ONE HUNDRED UP.

One hundred miles of the mad, virtually blind dash were now behind them. There were still forty miles to go; and there were still the giant, long-range coastal guns to pass at the Woosung forts.

At four o'clock Kerans, peering ahead into the night, suddenly saw that *Amethyst* was running straight for a junk which was sailing without lights. They were almost upon it, and nothing could be done to prevent a crash.

As the ship sliced the junk neatly in two *Amethyst* shook from bow to stern.

Frank had been taking benzedrine tablets regularly. He was the coxswain now, and there was no one to relieve him at the wheel. He had a bucket beside him in case it should be needed. Now and then he was brought a cup of tea and a sandwich. He was not able to see anything from the wheelhouse, but steered steadily as Kerans commanded.

Suddenly the ship trembled with shock.

"We're hit!" Frank thought.

Then Kerans' voice flowed coolly out of the voice-pipe. "That is a junk, that was," he said.

Frank exhaled heavily.

Meanwhile H.M.S. *Concord* moved into the wide mouth of the Yangtse to cover *Amethyst* if she came under the fire of the heavy Woosung guns.

"Come quick," Kerans signalled to her.

He could see searchlights sweeping the water far ahead, probing the thinning night. The sky directly above was still black, but far to the east he could see a lighter strip of heaven. He still hoped to get out of the river before dawn. The Yangtse was getting wider all the time.

As the ship neared the forts Kerans moved her as far out from the south shore as he felt was safe.

"Train B-gun on the forts," he ordered—"just in case." The single four-inch weapon was no match for the great nine-inchers of the forts. The men on the upper deck put on their tin-hats and waited.

Then, as they came to a point directly opposite the watchdog forts, a searchlight probed past the ship.

It stopped.

It swept slowly, carefully back. Kerans watched it, fascinated and afraid.

The searchlight passed on.

The first shoots of dawn were spreading across the sky, and *Amethyst* was as far out into the river towards the north shore as navigating hazards allowed. The Communists could not after all have spotted them. The big guns did not fire.

Kerans' voice burst over the intercom.

"I want every man to give everything he has for the last leg," he said. His voice sounded almost cheerful.

Down in the dim light of the engineroom Williams grinned. He was very tired. Perspiration was running down his face and his body, as it had done all night. "We'll make it now," he said to no one in particular. "We damn' well will."

Ormrod climbed up the ladder to the upper deck to see where they were. He came clattering down again. "There's a destroyer in sight," he shouted. "I think it's one of ours!" His voice cracked with excitement.

A couple of minutes later some one yelled exuberantly down the hatch, "*Concord* in sight!"

Williams did not try to hide the quaver in his voice. "All

right," he said. "We'll go up, one at a time, and have a look. Winfield, you take it first."

The cool air hit Winfield like a wall of water. He stepped out on to the quarterdeck and looked round. *Concord* was very near to them now. He could see the grinning, excitedly pleased faces of her crew, welcoming *Amethyst* back to the fleet. A great cheer swelled across the water. Then *Concord* turned, her bow pushing into the wide, safe mouth of the river towards the near-by open sea.

Winfield saw that, around him, some of *Amethyst's* men were crying, quite openly and without shame. Then he put a hand to his face and discovered that his own cheeks were wet. He didn't care. He didn't care at all.

In the chartroom McNamara grinned at Bryson. "Isn't it wonderful?" he said.

Bryson's lips moved, but no sound came out. He had talked himself quite hoarse over the voice-pipe, shouting the depths up to Kerans, and now he could not speak at all. But the look on his face, the sheer relieved joy on it, spoke much louder than any words.

Frank, in the wheelhouse, thought, "I've been in the Navy for twenty-four years, but I've never felt like this before."

Now Kerans sent his last message to the C.-in-C. He dictated it proudly to French:

HAVE REJOINED THE FLEET. AM SOUTH OF WOO-SUNG. NO DAMAGE OR CASUALTIES. GOD SAVE THE KING.

They were out.